OLDE
CHARLIE FARQUHARSON'S
TESTAMENT

is the propitty of

_____

_____

_____

OLDE
CHARLIE FARQUHARSON'S
TESTAMENT

from Jennysez to Jobe
and
After Words

as tolled to
Don Harron

Gage Publishing
Toronto, Vancouver, Calgary, Montreal

Design by FORTUNATO AGLIALORO

Illustrations by GUSTAVE DORÉ

adapted by FORTUNATO AGLIALORO

Canadian Cataloguing in Publication Data

Harron, Donald, 1924-
Olde Charlie Farquharson's Testament

ISBN 0-7715-9900-5 bd.   ISBN 0-7715-9901-3 pa.

1. Bible. O.T. — Anecdotes, facetiae, satire,
etc. I. Title.

PS8565.A78053   C817'.5'4   C78-001390-5
PR9199.3.H376053

Printed and bound in Canada

1 2 3 4 5 HR 82 81 80 79 78

For Kelley

Famly Tree

Muther

Grandfather

Grammuther

Father

Uther
Grandfather

Uther
Grammuther

Antsandunkels

Meturnal

Pawturnal

_____   _____
_____   _____
_____   _____
_____   _____
_____   _____

Berths

_____

_____

_____

_____

Mirages

_____

_____

_____

_____

Deths

_____

_____

_____

_____

Babee's Eyedentficayshun

Naim _____

Wait _____

Lenth _____

Culler Eyes _____

Culler Hare _____

Cumpleckshun _____

Uther Dada _____

_____

_____

_____

Deevelpmint

Naim _____

Hed Heldup _____   Turnover Aloan _____

Setup Aloan _____   Crawl _____

Speek Furst _____   Tuck Furstep _____

Cut Furstooth _____   Cut Resta teeth _____

Uther Inresting Facks _____

Needels on Record   Daits

Hoop-in coff _____   _____

Dipfeeria _____   _____

Smallpocks _____   _____

Tetnuss _____   _____

Tiefoyed Feever _____   _____

Ottografts

Muther

Father

_____

Docter

Nerse

_____

Berth Sertifficut File

Dait: _____

Sired by: _____

Dammed Out of: _____

Plaice: _____

Babee Naimd Fur: _____

Crissnin Dait: _____

Cherch _____

Clurjyman _____

Godpairnts _____

_____

Let's have some light here

The First Book of Moeziz, called

JENNYSEZ

CHAPTER 1

A t the start there wasn't a thing. That'd be yer Void.

2 Dark too. Absoloot kayoss. So God decided to do something about it

3 He sed, Let's have some Light here. And there was. Right off. But there still weren't nothing to look at.

4 He kept yer Dark too. Now He had two things going fer Him. Night and Day.

5 He had the one foller the other so's He could keep track. That was all in one day's work.

6 The second day God sed, We need some kind of Firmermint in the middle of all this water. (Don't ask me where the water come frum in the first place.) But the Firmermint would shore up some of the water from the rest of the water.

7 So God did it.

8 The Firmermint part He called Hevven. That was quite enuff fer the second day.

9 But there was still all that loose water. So He gathered most of what was under Hevven and called them the Seeze.

10 So far, not a thing to stand on. God thot, what on erth will I do? That's when He let yer dry land come up. And He sed, That's good.

11 Then God sed, Let's get organized here.

12 Erth brot up grass, grass brot up herb, herb brot up seed, seed brung trees and trees brung froot. That was good.

13 So far, three days.

14 Then God sed, We need lights at night too. So He made the Moon fer a nitelite. God figgered that to go fer years.

15 He put some side-lites in too, not so much to lite things up but to give the place a bit of a glow.

16 That'd be yer Stars.

17 The Moon and Stars worked nights, and the Sun was put on the day-shift.

18 God thot that set-up should work out all right.

19 That was yer fourth day. And nite, by that time.

20 God sed, Look here, there's nothin' doing in these waters. Better stir things up a bit, git some creechers moving. Air's kind of empty too. Might as well fowl it up.

21 And He dun a whale of a job down to yer smallest minny.

22 Then they was all told to git at it being frootfull and multyplying.

23 That day'd be yer fifth.

24 All this time, on erth, nothing doing. All that grass and herb and nothing to pastyer on it.

25 So He called forth cattels, and beests, and other creepy things. Nothing bad about that.

26 Then God took a aweful chance. He sed, Somebuddy has got to soopervise all them dumb minions of Mine, on erth, under water, and

even pretty well all up in the air, too. (Sept the Angels, and don't ask me where they all of a sudden come frum.)

27 So God thot up somebuddy to look jist like Him.

28 He called this fella, Man, and told him the same thing about being frootfull and multyplying, even tho' so far there was only one of him.

29 And God sed to Man, The place is yours.

30 Take care of it for Me, and take care of yerself, too.

31 And God thot all that was good. He was tired. He'd bin at it six days.

CHAPTER 2

That's about it, He sed.

2 The seventh day He jist took off.

3 He thot everybuddy else should take it off, too.

5 So far, no rain. And none of yer soil had bin turned over neether.

6 So God sent a mist up from the erth, becuz He figgered it was dew.

7 Maybe that's becuz Man had bin made outa dust, and didn't know anything about watering plants.

8 He didn't have to. The Lord give him a green Garden that supplied all his food. That's why it was called yer Garden of Eatin'. Straight from dust onto Welfare.

9 God grew trees to put Man in the shade. Most trees was very ornery, but two was extra-speshul, private propperty, outa bounds, yer Tree of Life-Everafter and the other one of Good'n-Evil.

10 Man didn't even have to water the Garden. Two rivers dun the job, yer Tie-grass and yer You-fraidees.

15 Man's job was soft. Green-skeeper.

16 And God tole Man he cud have the produce of every tree on the lot.

17 Sept one. "Don't go snitchin' froot offa the Tree of Good'n-Eevil, or the ladder will befall you."

18 Man didn't seem too happy. So God thot he should have a help-mate.

19 Meentime, Man was gittin' frendly with all the other beests, countin' them up, and givin' them pet names. He even give hisself a name ... Add'em.

20 So God thot it was time to add to Add'em

21 First He put him to sleep, and wile he was out and under, God yanked out one of his ribs.

22 And wen God had it all dun up nice, He brung her to Add'em.

23 Add'em took one look and sed, "Oh good God. Let's call her Woe-man."

24 On account of the ribbing, man and woe-man was one flesh. Without any pairnts or in-laws it shoulda bin a ideel arrangement.

25 By the by, they was both bare as birds. Didn't bother the neether of them one little bit.

CHAPTER 3

Speaking about creepy things, one of them that God had made, was yer Serpint. No legs, but lotsa branes, turned out to be a reel Mover. First thing he dun was stir things up in the orcherd.

2 It slithered over to the Woe-man and sed, "How come you don't eat offa this here tree?"

God ribs Add'em

3 She sed, "On accounta it's poizoned, we cud likely become a ded issyuh."

5 And that snake in the grass tole her, "Open yer eyes, girl, you don't know a good thing when you see it. (Or eevil eether, come to that.)

6 Grab one and git wise to yerself," sed the snake. So she grabbed and et, and even shuvved one into her husbin's mouth, saying, "How'd you like them apples?"

7 One bite and Add'em had his eyes open. He took one look at his wife and notissed she weren't wearing a stitch. That's when the cover-up started. Both of them beeting around the bush fer sumthing to hide ther dirty shames. Before this, they wouldn't have cared a fig.

8 They even hid from God who was taken his mid-day shady walk.

9 But you know you can't hide from Him.

10 Add'em sed, "Sorry, Sir, but you cot us without our cloze on."

11 "Cloze?" sed God. "Who ever told you you was naked in the first place? Wait a minit. You two bin pickin' apples?"

12 Sez Add'em, "I jist et. The little Woe-man has bin pickin'."

13 And the little Woe-man sed, "Yer obeedient serpint sed it would be all right."

14 And the Lord sed full sore, "Down on yer belly, you reptile! Hentsforth I don't wanta see you fer dust, fer that's all yer gonna git to eat.

15 And from now every Woe-man is gonna screem when she sees one of you. Morn likely stomp on you with her hi-heels!"

16 To the Woe-man He sed, "You've reely dun it now. Addem's in charge frum now on, and yer in charge of the kids." "What's kids?" sez the Woe-man. "You'll find out," sed God, "to yer everlasting Sorrow."

17 And God sed to Add'em, "Frum now on, yer gonna work fer a living.

18 I jist thot up something new fer this place. It's called Weeds.

19 I made you frum dust, so you may as well work by the sweat of yer brow. Dust plus sweat is Dirt, and that's all you are to me from now on."

20 Add'em didn't say too much to that. Frum now on, he deecided to call his wife Eave, on accounta she was the cause of him being dumped on frum above.

21 Both of them stood there shivrin' in frunt of ther Maker, so He finely took a little piddy on them, and give them gote-coats fer to cover ther goose-bumps.

22 But God figgered if they broke the leese once, they'd try it agin. Soon's He turned his back, they'd be up the tree agin, the one lets you live ferever.

23 That's why He four-closed, and put up the No Tresspassing sine and kicked them out. Add'em and Eave had gambled and now it was yer Pairadice Lost.

24 And to make sure they staid out, God put one of yer Cheery Bims at the east end of the Park, discurridgin' visiters with one of them Flaming Sords.

4

This Gardin is closed to Visitors

CHAPTER 4

There was nothing else to do. So Add'em and Eave started to bare children. First one bore was Cane, and Eave sed, "I have got me a man frum the Lord." (They come full-groan in them days, I spose.)

2 It happened agin. She bare Able. Them boys grew fast. First thing you knew Cane was a-hoeing and Able a-sheeping.

3 But both boys was smart enuff to know where they come frum, and took up a little colleckshun to show God ther depreciation. Cane bein' a farmer, brung things frum outa the ground and outa yer tree.

4 Able, yer sheepish brother, brung along one of his fattest lambs. God liked him best.

5 Cane probly figgered on his Maker being a Vegetary-Aryan, and was hurt when God didn't seem to cotton too much to the presents he was offring.

6 God sed, "What are you moping about with yer face on the floor for?

7 You win some, you lose some. That's life. Some days it goes like that, what more can I tell you? Frum now on Able's gonna be the straw-boss."

8 Cane didn't talk back to God, but he sure had a few words with his brother. And some action too. When he got thru, his brother had bin dis-Abled fer good.

9 "Seen Able, Cane?" seth God a liddle later. Cane sed, "You per-moted him to Hed-keeper. It's not my job to keep track of him." Seth God. "It's all famly Cane. Aren't you yer Keeper's brother?"

10 Jist then, the ghost of Able cried out undyground. God herd. "Oh, oh, Cane! What have you dun, now?

11 Don't bother to tell me. I awreddy know. I don't like to do this but what I'm going to have to do is curse, and what I'm going to curse is you. Frum now on fergit about farming, becuz nothing is coming up fer you.

12 Git moving."

13 Poor Cane cried out, "How did I know he was gonna die! It's new. Nobody ever died before.

14 I'm a farmer, not a travlin man. How do I know I won't die too?"

15 Seth the Lord, "If anybuddy does what you dun to yer brother, he's a marked man." And jist to show Cane what he meant, He give him a after-berth-mark on his fore-head.

16 Cane went off East, to be a far-out farmer in a sleepy little place name of the Land of Nod.

17 He settle down, become Citty-zen Cane, never dun too well at the tilling but sure got good at rearing. Raised a little Cane every year. (It don't say who he married, but it hadda be his sister, if you insest on finding out.)

18 They had a boy Eunoch, and in time he had some more of his own, a hole cityful in fact, which is conseev-able.

19 Ther grate-grate-grate gransun was Lammick who was the first to of took two wives, Ada and Zilla. (This is the first mention of the change-over to polygmy instead of monotony.)

20 Ada, she bore Jawball, who become the patron father of cattel-

Cain Disables

men and everybuddy else who lives intense.

21 His brother, Jueball become the incester of all them as become harp and organ handlers, known in them days as lires and pipers.

22 Zilla, she raised Tooball Cane, hed instructer and chief forger in yer brass and ironworks.

25 Even old Add'em never give up after Able got Caned. He waited till he was 130 and then Eave got him another boy, Seth, named after the way the Lord was in a habit of speaking to him.

CHAPTER 5

The Add'ems famly started to spred out after a time on account of it was gittin' a little crowded.

4 Main problem was everybuddy was sich long livers they seemed to of hung around ferever.

5 Add'em he got to nine thirty before he let go. (That'd be nine hunderd thirty.)

6-26 These versus is a cattlehog of Add'ems close deesendents. Most of them never had any children till they was well past three scored and ten, which shows how shy they was in them days.

27 The all-time long-time titel-holder was a grate grandsun of Add'ems called Methusalaw, clocked out at 969. He got his first boy, Lammick when he was 187. Imagine sitting on the porch fer 782 yeers after that, killin' time and swattin' flies.

28 Lammick waited till he was 182 before he had his son, Noah. But that's another story.

CHAPTER 6

Talk about crowds. It come to sich a pass that people were still mul-typlying when they were hundreds of yeers old.

2 It warnt a case of wife-swoppin' becuz you could have as many as you want.

3 God thot enuff was enuff, and put a time-limit on Man: a hunderd and twenny yeers, tops.

4 Men was not only around long in them days, they was big too. Big, nothing, they was what we call Giants.

5 Big in wickedness too. God saw that right off.

6 He was even sorry now He'd started the hole thing.

7 So He figgered on canselling mebby four outa that first six days work.

8 Everybuddy was to get wiped out. Exsept Noah and all in the famly.

9 Noah was in step with God, just, perfect, and lived with Grace.

10 Noah was proud of Hem, Sham and Jetpath, "my three sons."

11 God saw that they was good. But fer the rest of the planit, things genrully looked bout as bad as they do now.

12 God figgered the trubble was plution, and Man was the cheef pluter.

13 He told Noah, "We have reached the flesh-point. It's time to faze people out.

14 If I was you, Noah, I'd git me a Ark." "What's a Ark?" "Never mind. Git go-fer wood, quite a few cord, and to make sure she's water-tite, make yer pitch all over it.

15 Better be a big one while yer at it. Say three hunderd by fifty by thirty cube bits.

16 Git a roof over yer heds, make a winder, and a side door. Better have threc story down, to take care of Bee Deck, yer Sea Deck, and yer Steeredge.

17 You'll spend a lotta time blowdecks cuz it's gonna be the wet season fer quite some time, none of that inter-mitten stuff. And SWIM-MIN LESSENS WON'T HELP.

18 Do as I say, and yer bunch will be snug as a bug.

19 The animals has to be took in as well. Jist two of a kind, mind. Better make it two of allsorts or the holc thing will be in vane."

20 "You mean two of every blamed livin thing, inclooding black flys and muskeeters?"

21 "Jist git on with it," spake God. "Better lode up on supplys, too, to last you fer a fortynite."

22 Noah dun it.

CHAPTER 7

"Time," sed God. "You and the good brothers and yer inlaws and all that livestock, inside!

2 By the by, better make it seven of a kind. Sept for the ones what don't clean themselves, jist let two of them in, no sense making more work fer yerselves. And you kin skip the fish. With what's coming they kin take care of themselfs.

3 As fer yer fouls of the air, they kin come in sevens too." (It don't reecord what Noah sed to this, but henhouses is gritty work.)

4 "Once in, I'll turn on the shower. I figger on forty days, inclooding' the nites. That should put us over the top."

5 Noah sed nuthin. Jist dun as he was told.

6 He was six hundred yeers old, and knew enuff to come in outa the rain.

7 And the little woman and the sons and ther little women climbed in behind him.

8 Folleyed close behind by all them creepin' beests and fouls, both yer cleans and yer dirtys.

9 They hadda line-up 2 by 2, a boy and a girl frum eech speeshies. (I think they musta fergot about the sevenses by this time.)

10 And it come to pass. Water after seven days.

11 That was Febyouary 17th, accordin to Noah. That'd be the day yer fountings of the deep broke up and the winders of Hevven opened with one big splash.

12 It kep up steddy fer close on to six weeks.

18 That Ark floted, thank God.

19 Everything else went under.

20 Even yer mountings.

21 As fur as you could see there was water, with bubbles comin up fer a short time.

22 Everybuddy left offa the Ark got a nosefull and quit.

23 Noah and his bunch was left high'ndry.

24 This went on till July 16. That's a hundred and fifty days.

CHAPTER 8

G od dint ferget yer Arkers. He made a big wind pass over the waters fer to asswage them.

2 He stopped up yer fountings of the deep, and slammed shut the winders of Hevven. This cut yer water off.

3 Lotsa drane-edge fer quite a wile. Dunno where it went. Mebby God made the Erth round to take care of all that run-off.

4 The mountings showed up first, and that's where yer Ark come to a full stop, top of Mount Arrer-root.

5 From then on it was all downhill. But it took ten munths fer to disembArk.

6 Noah he was reddy to step out soon's the rain stopped. First thing he dun was open a winder, and glad to do it.

7 He took one of them foul offa ther nest and set it outside. This was one of yer ravins. Fool thing flapped off and never came back.

8 "Nevermore," thot Noah. He sent off a hoaming pidgin insted. (In them days pidgins was called yer Doves.)

9 That Dove musta wondered where yer Ravin went, becuz there weren't no place to set a dry foot.

10 Noah took her in, wiped her feet, set her out a week later.

11 This time she never come empty-footed. It was way after dark but in she come, a olive leef in her beek. Noah figgered somethin was stickin up above yer water-line.

12 Week later he shove yer Dove out agin. This time she never come back. Probly met another dove.

13 It was next New Yeer's Day before Noah finely took the roof off. Musta figgered it ain't gonna rain no more.

14 But things below was still gummy and gooey. She warnt dry enuff to step out on till Feb. 27, morn a yeer since they had all incarserrated themselves.

15 Finely God Hisself spake up.

16 "Time to rise and shine. Git yer wife and the 3 sons and go forth.

17 Tell them to bring the wife too, and all them fleshy beests, and foul. Tell every creepy thing the ground is dry, it's time to multyply."

19 They cleered that Ark in no time.

20 First thing Noah dun was make a Alter, fer to give thanks. He took bits off every clean beest, and were they ever burnt up.

21 God could smell it, and thot it was good. He dint feel like cursing anymore. Man was made in His image, but frum now on, He wasn't expecting too much frum him.

22 God put back all of the wether, yer drys and yer lows, yer heet and yer cold, so Man could be in season agin.

CHAPTER 9

A nd God give Noah and Sons the rite to fill up the erth agin.

2 "And member, yer in charge of all this livestock." (That musta bin easier to do outside of the Ark.)

3 "Everything is fair game.

4 Jist drane the bleedin things first.

5 You fellows are My beests, mind, and yer life blud is in My hands, so don't be sprized if I ask fer it sometimes.

They missed the boat

6 That don't meen you kin go round sheddin eech others. That's strickly off-limits.

7 So don't subtrack from eech other, jist multyply."

8 God drew up a leese between Him and Noah and all his seeds.

9 It was a gennlemen's agreemint, no signin on the dotted line.

10 Nobuddy in that Ark could rite anyways, speshly the beests.

11 God sed, "No more hi-jinks frum you, no more high water from Me.

12 And that goes fer all yer fewcher generations."

13 And to show them the bad wether was over, up in the sky He put a rainbow, jist to remind them that He is somewhere over it.

14 God sed, "That don't meen a perpetchul dry spell, but frum now on, every cloud's gonna have a silver, red, yella, green, blue, and purpull lining.

15 Jist to remind both of us not to overdo this water thing, agin.

17 Everybuddy agreed?" "Whut ever you say, Sir."

18 Noah started up agin at the same old stand, but his boys felt differnt.

19 They wanted to spred out fer therselfs, all over yer erth. Sept Noah's son Hem. He only wanted a spred as fur as the land of Cane-in.

20 First thing Noah raised after his three sons was a Vinyard. And he used the first froots of his vines fer to git drunk.

21 There he was flat out in his tent, tighterna a drum, with no close on.

22 His son Hem peeked at this, on accounta Noah left the flap open.

He went out and tole on his father to Sham and Jetpath, but his two brothers was not amews.

23 They brung a blankit and backed into the tent fer the cover-up, as they did not wanna see ther old Dad laid out like that.

24 Noah woke up, not too hungover to figger what his youngest son had dun, when he was out of it in the alltogether.

25 Noah curst Hem as far as the land of Cane-in. Cut him outa his will, and let him be hired man to his brothers.

28 After that Noah was a broke-in man, only lived 350 more yeers, died at 950. (Whutever happen to them freeze controls on Old Age a wile back?)

CHAPTER 10

After yer Flud, Noah's boys dint let no genration gap grow below ther feet. They had a flud of ther own—big crop of kinfolk.

2 First off, Jetpath had sons of his own: Gomer, Maygog, Mad-Eye, Javin', Twoball, Me-shack, and Tire-as.

3 Gomer he had a pile, too: Ashcan-azz, Rip Path, ToeGarmaw.

4 Javin' dun good with his boys: Ely Shaw, Tarsheesh, Kitt'em, and Do-down-im.

5 It was these fellas popillated yer erth. Some of them even ended up Jentiles, but don't ask me how.

6 Hem, the displeased person, even he had a buncha sons: Cush, Fut, Eejippt, and Canin'. Sounds like they lit out and foundered a few places is still around today.

7 Cush got sons hisself.

Noah cuts off his Hem

8 Best known was Dimrod.

9 The Mitey Hunter.

10 He was mostly mitey in Babble, a town over there in Shiner hard by Eareck.

11 Then he lit out fer Assearya and bilt Ninnyvuh.

12 That was oney a start. He bilt other cities too. Not what we call yer slow develper.

13-32 Other things develped too. Mostly peeple becoming crowds. Quite a spred frum one little Ark.

CHAPTER 11

No matter how well-spred everybuddy was, they all spoke the same langridge.

2 But most people took a shine to yer plane of Shiner. That seemed to be the place to hang around. It was nice but kinda flat.

3 Everybuddy sed, let's bild us a hy-rise. We got bricks to burn.

4 Let's add morter and fresh slime, and mebby the place will reech up to Hevven. Keep us in touch with Him. Sorta a Community-cation Tower.

5 When they had dun it part way, God come down to inspeck the works.

6 He thot peeple were startin' to git above themselfs tryna move into His naberhood. God thot, "Give 'em anuther inch and they'll think they're roolers."

7 He put His hex on that Babble rabble and scrabbled ther tongues so they all spoke differnt.

8 That dun it. When nobuddy could git the hang of anybuddy else's lingo, all them mixt-up peeple climbed down offa ther hy-rize and becum Seppertists.

9 They all went abroad, becuz everybuddy at home was forners anyway. Dunno wat happen to that hy-rize. Musta becum a Ex-communication Tower.

10-27 Sham staid tho' and hung around fer generation and generation, and generation.

28 Out of it come lots of others, but mostly a leeder called Abie-ham.

29 Abie-ham married Sairy.

30 But she was barn. No childern.

31 Abie-ham decided to try his luck eltsware. Sairy come along fer the ride.

CHAPTER 12

God figgered it was time to find anuther lone, saltery man whom He could trust. He settled on Abie-ham who had jist come from the city of Er and settled in Haran. God told him to git unsettled and start movin agin.

2 "If you do, I'll show you some nice country and make you father of it.

3 I'll take care of you and yorn, and if anybuddy gives any of youse any trouble boy will I ever take care of him."

4 Abie-ham was 75, but, fer God's sake, he packed up his wife and all his cattels, and took the lot with him.

5 Lot was his brother's son, and he come along too.

6 They passed thru the land of Cane-in without stoppin' too long on accounta the place was loaded with Canin'-nites.

Babble Towers, the first hy-rize

7 But God sed, "This here's the land I have pick out fer yer deesendents."

8 Abie-ham marked the spot with a alter.

9 After that he kep going acrost yer Neg-ebb dessert.

10 Nobuddy in the sand bizness was doin' too good, so Abie-ham percyveered as far's Ejippt.

11 Before they went thru Ejippt customs, he sed to his wife Sairy, "Yer a good lookin woman, Sair . . .

12 These Ejippters will take one look at you, and probably knock me off.

13 So if anybuddy asks yer status, say yer my sister."

14 They sure notissed Sairy, them Ejippshuns.

15 They told ther boss Faro bout her. She was ast over.

16 After Faro dated her, Abie-ham dun well out of it. Sheep, oxin, cammels, menservints, madeservints, not to menshun he-and-she asses.

17 God, He was fit to be tied. He brung plaigs on Faro's house, and let him know why.

18 Faro called Abie-ham ina rush. "What are you doin' to me?

19 That was no sister, that was yer wife. Now you take her back and git outa here!"

CHAPTER 13

Abie-ham took Sairy and Lot and a lot more back across the dessert.

2 He kept all of Faro's presents.

4 He went back to where he set up that alter.

5 Lot come along so he cud be in the famly's way, but he was gittin' tired of tag-in-along.

6 He had herds of his own, and dint see much future in Abie-ham's pasture.

7 When his cowboys started to fite with Abie's cowboys he thot it was time to seprate.

8 Abie-ham sed, "We're famly. Let's raise cattel insted of our hands agin each other.

9 Pick yerself out a nice lot, Lot, and I'll make do with the rest."

10 Lot dun jist that. Quite a spred he picked too. The hole of yer Jordan vallee.

12 Abie-ham got stuck with yer hi-ground.

13 Lot moved his wife and cows to a nice, low green place called Sod'em. Sept it wernt all that nice, in fack, it was downright wicked.

14 God sed to Abie-ham, "Never mind that lot. You keep yer eyes up, and away frum all that dirt.

16 You cum frum dust, and you'll git back to dust, but in the meentimes I'm gonna make as many of yer tribe as there is dust around here, howdya like that?"

18 Abie-ham went out and bilt hisself another alter.

CHAPTER 14

Things was never too good in Sod'em and they was worse in Begorrah.

9 Sides the usual hanky-panks, sibble war was goin' on, and the score was four kings aginst five.

10 Part of that Vally was the pits and some of them Kings jist natcherly fell into it.

11 The rest fled to yer mountings.

12 Lot got took along with them, poor sod.

13 Abie-ham herd about it.

14 He chased after Lot as fur as Dan with 318 train men.

15 He divvied up his force, dun a smash-and-grab nite job, put them to rout, and folleyed in pursoot.

16 He cum back frum Dan tuckered but with all Lot's stole goods and Lot too.

17 The King of Sod'em herd all about this, and wanted to meet Abie-ham.

18 The King of Sail'em did too. He was a part-time priest on the side so he brung along bread and wine.

19 He blest Abie-ham fer delivring all them enmys.

20 Abie-ham musta bin touched, fer he give that king ten persent of what he netted.

21 Yer Sod'em King sed, "Thanks fer delivring my peeple, but you got the goods, so keep 'em."

23 But Abie-ham dint want so much as a sandle-strap. Nobuddy was gonna call him a war profitear.

24 "Jist give us our rashins, and call it quits."

CHAPTER 15

God come to Abie-ham in a dubble vision and sed, "Good work, and soon you'll git yer reewards."

2 Abie-ham sed, "I don't like to be pushy, but how kin I found a hole nation when I can't even git started on my own family?"

5 God took him outside and sed, "See them stars? That's how many offspring yer gonna have runnin round here."

8 Abie-ham sed, "It better start soon. I'm gittin on."

9 So God ordered up a heffer, a she-gote and a ram, all in yer 3 yeer-old class, plus one dove and a pidgin.

10 Abie-ham rounded them all up, cut them in two, sept the birds.

11 Birds of prey cum along sniffin at the carkasses but Abie-ham druv them off.

12 Long tord sundown a grate darkness started to fall (natcherly). Abie-ham fell into adeep asleep.

13 God peered in Abie-ham's dreems. "Here's the pitcher. Yer peeple is gonna be on the move agin and things is gonna be tuff fer the next four hundred yeers.

14 But don't pay no mind. Them forners that enslaves yer peeple is gonna have it even tuffer.

15 As fer you persnally, yer good fer a fair spell yet.

16 Yer gonna rust in peace. Four genrations later, yer tribe will be back on their old stompin ground. Garnteed."

17 To seel the bargin, a little smoking pot and a big flame-in torch passed 'tween them.

18 This was the cuvvinant 'tween Abie-ham and his Lord.

CHAPTER 16

But no tribe yet. Sairy was still barn of children. But she had a hired girl name of Hagger.

2 So she sed to Abie-ham, "It's time to try somethin else. Namely, Hagger."

3 Abie-ham, he harkened to that.

4 As the sayin goes, he went in, and she come out of it with child. Plus a sneer on her face fer Sairy.

5 Sairy complaned to Abie-ham

bout the sass she was gitten frum the hired help.

6 Abie-ham backed off with: "Yer still the boss, Sare. Do with her what you like, as I have did." So Sairy kicks Hagger out, regardless of her famly way.

7 Hagger lit out fer the wild parts, finely stopped fer a spring drink.

8 One of God's Angels cot up with her, "Where you goin so fast?"

9 Hagger sed she was fixin to go any place where old Sairy was not. That Angel sed, "You better go back and punch in. Sairy's yer boss. Besides, yer carryin' the father of yer country.

11 That's a reel boy you've got in yuh. Call him Ish-male.

12 He's gonna be one wild ass of a man. His hand agin every man, and every man's hand agin him, so yuh better be prepared to give him, every once in a wile, the back of yores."

15 When Hagger finely bore Ish-male to Abie-ham he was purt neer 86. (Abie-ham, not Ishmale.)

CHAPTER 17

God peered before Abie-ham agin when he was 99.

2 Still talkin' about multyplying and been frootful, God was.

3 Abie-ham fell on his face.

4 God sed, "Jist keep up our agreemint and you'll be hed of a multytude of nations. Here's the rools.

10 First thing everybuddy's gotta do when ther 8 days old is git sircumsize.

11 This is dun thru the fourskins. In yer case it'll be rettero-active.

14 Anybuddy won't do it, git it cut off. That's all."

15 Abie-ham sed, "What about Sairy?" "Big plans. She'll be a king's mother."

16 Abie-ham fell on his face and laffed. "Dear God, Sairy's ninety and I'm purt neer a hunderd. What do you expeck?

18 Besides, what's wrong with Ish-male?"

19 "Ish-male was awright fer a start," sed God, "but Sairy's gonna have her own boy, call him I-sick.

20 Ish-male's gonna multyply and cum forth with 12 princes, but I-sick's the one I'm countin on, and he's comin this time next yeer."

22 But Abie-ham was too busy soopervising the sircumsizing fer to prepair fer little I-sick.

23 Every member of his tribe was sore afrayed, but not so much then as mebby afterwards.

CHAPTER 18

God He never fergot about the I-sick projeck. One day He come before Abie-ham sitten in front of his tent flaps in the heat. It was so wavy hot God looked like three peeple at once.

4 Abie-ham sed, "Come in, wash yer feet, rest yerself. I'll git you bread and milk before you pass on."

6 Abie-ham run back into the tent, told Sairy to kneed some meel and whip up a cake. He got a servint to pick a calf and prepair it, with curds and milk along the wey.

8 Abie-ham stood by them wile the three of them (who was still reely God) et.

God cums to Abie-ham in triplacut

9 They (God) ast after the wearabouts of his wife Sairy. "In the back of yer tense," sez Abie-ham.

10 Then the three Lords sed, "Be back next spring to have a look at her brannew, bouncin baby boy I-sick." Sairy, as was her want, was lissening behind the tent door in a flap.

11 Sairy thot fer sure she was past all that.

12 She started to laff at the thot of it starting all over agin.

13 God herd her, wundered what she was laffin' at.

14 Becuz nothin is too hard fer the Lord.

15 Sairy got scairt, clamed she never laffed.

16 God sed, "Oh yes you did, but if you think we're kidding now, wait till next spring."

17 Then God (all three of Him) got up and headed tord Sod'em. Abie-ham went with Them part way.

18 God wundered, shall I let Abie-ham in on what I'm up to over to Sod'em.

19 I better, since he is gonna be bout all I have left after I git thru.

20 So God spake up about how things was going to pot in Sod'em and He wanted to see fer Hisself how downhill things was going, and also mebby clock in on G'morrah, that other Plane City.

21 "If ther sins is grave, they'll all end up in it soonern they expeck," He told Abie-ham.

23 Abie-ham knew God meant it. He dun it before with the water treetment. So he ast God, "Will you destroy all the rite-yuss peeple along with the backsiders?"

24 "Rite-yuss?" seth God. "Name fifty and the hole place is spared!"

25 Abie-ham thunk hard. "Well . . . mebby forty-five?"

27 He was thinkin all the time, oh dear Lord who am I to take it upon me to dicker with Him bein' myself meerly dust and ashes, wich is what all them sinners is gonna end up as, incloodin' my good brother's boy Lot.

26 "Check forty-five good'uns then!" God sed.

29 "Sposin' forty?" "Forty'll do!"

30 "How bout thirty?" "Take thirty!"

31 "Would you bleeve twenny?" "Why not?"

32 "Say ten, that'll be my last offer." "Even ten! Yer on!" sez God and went on His way to find ten good men, if true.

CHAPTER 19

God musta got fed up with Sod'em cuz He dallygated two Angels to do the cleenup.

2 Lot seen them first, and ast them in fer to spend the nite after they washed the dust off ther feet and wings. But them Angels had figgered on spendin' the nite walkin' the streets. Lot tole them Sod'em wasn't that kinda street-walkin' town.

3 Insted Lot give them a feest of unlevy-ed bred.

4 Jist before they all turned in, there was a knocking at the front of Lot's door. Turns out a buncha Sod'emites had herd ther was new boys in town, wanted to meet them.

5 To the last man they called out, "Don't be a hawg, Lot. We wanna

git to know them too." (In them Bib-lickle days "git to know" meant morn it does now.)

6 Lot knew what they was after, come out hisself, but shut the door after him.

7 When he told them to go home, they started to act nasty (which was par fer the corse fer Sod'em.)

8 Lot went as fur as he could to be nice, even offert the crowd two of his dotters (who were no-vices) if they would leave these heavenly fellas alone.

9 But this Sod'em crowd wasn't intrusted in girls and told Lot to stand back or they'd stove in the frunt of his vestybule.

10 They purt neer broke down the door too, when all of a sudden a anjellic hand come out frum behind that door and Lot was whisked indoors on a wing and a prayer.

11 They musta threw some angel dust in the crowd's eyes, too, because all them preeverts was left groping fer eech other in the dark.

12 Then them Angels took wing, but before take-off they told Lot's lot to cleer out too fer ther was gonna be a hot time in the old town tonite.

14 When Lot tole his family who them misteeryuss winged creechers was, they jist laffed at him.

15 But when them Angels' torches got lit they was consoomed with intrest.

16 To make sure Lot dint linger longer, them Angels swooped down and airlift him and his wife and two dotters outa town.

17 "Wich way do we go?" sed Lot. "Hit fer the hills, flee, and don't

look back" sung them torch-singeing Angels.

23 Nothing happened that nite.

24 But when yer sun rize next time, you never seen sich hail come outa Hevven. Only this time it was firin' brimstones. And the Lord rained supreem on them two twin sin cities ... burnt to a sinder yer hole valley and everything what grew, incloodin' yer Jordan wines.

26 Lot's bunch was safe, but his wife, nosey parker, jiss hadda have one more glimpse. One look and then she knew no more. From a piller of sassiety she had bin turned into the salt of the erth. Whenever cattel come by she was bound to take quite a licking.

27 Frum Abie-ham's pointa vue, the hole place went up in smoke.

28 That was God's punishmint. Them two towns had made complete ashes of themselfs.

29 There warnt much left, but Lot and two dotters, and one salty wife who was brung to a standstill.

30 Lot and the two dotters hadda sub-let a cave fer the time bein.

31 Them Lot girls was still true-blue Sod'emites. They was worried about a lack of illegible males after the holycost.

32 Fer all they knew, ther old father was probably the last man on erth. They figgered mebby the only way of gittin' in the family way was the famly way.

33 They got him titern a hoot owl and had ther own ways with ther father. (Most dotters do but this was differnt.) First born first, then the younger insested on her tern.

Miz Lot takes a backerd look jist before she gits salty

34 Lot he never knew what hit him fer nine hole munths.

35 And it hit all right. Both times. First dotter called hers Moe Ab and the second one Bon-Ami. They both should have called it Quits in the first place. I mean famlys are sposed to be close, but that's ridickluss.

CHAPTER 20

I dunno wether Abie-ham knew about his famly ties endin' up in sich a granny knot, but he lit out fer yer Negg-ebb dessert agin.

2 Funny bunch. He hisself started pullin' that "She's only my sister" rooteen with old Sairy, now gittin on fer ninety odd. But she musta bin still pretty becuz that lokel king A-bim-a-leg took one look, was took, and took her.

3 Abie-ham dun nothin, but God sent that King a nite message in a dreem, wich sed, "You have took the wrong woman, and you are a ded man. She was awreddy entered into holy acrimony with Abie-ham."

4 Luckly, A-bim-a-leg had not yet made the approach shot.

5 But he felt he was the one bin had on accounta the husbin kept saying, "She's my sister" and even the wife sed, "He's my brother." So sez A-bim-a-leg, "Deer God, what have I dun?"

6 "Nuthing," sez God. "It's a sin of o-mission, not trans-mission. But that's becuz I was around to cut in.

7 So give Abie-ham back the wife, fur he is my profit and kin do you good wile praying fer you."

10 A-bim-a-leg hot foot it over to Abie-ham. "Lissen, what were you thinking of when you dun this dumb thing?"

11 Sez Abie-ham, "I dun it becuz there was not feer of God in this place." Sez A-bim-a-leg, "Well, there sure is now. Don't ever do that sister bit agin."

12 "Besides," seth Abie-ham, "it's only haff a fib. She reely is my sister on my father's side, but not my mother's." Barks yer King, "I don't want to heer about it. What a famly!"

14 Abie-ham dun pritty well out of the hole mess. He got Sairy back, plus sheep, oxin, mail and femail, and the rite to set where he liked. Of sich is the feer of God.

16 Sairy come out of it with a thousand-piece silver set, which she turned right over to her "brother."

17 Then Abie-ham prayd fer God to heel A-bim-a-leg, considern he warnt too well-heeled any more. All he got out of it was more childern, on accounta God had closed every woom in A-bim-a-leg's house till the Sairy sityation cleered up.

CHAPTER 21

God kept his promise to yer impregnibble Sairy.

2 She had her spring baby on skedyule.

3 Abie-ham called him I-sick (mebby on accounta the way Sairy felt for the first few conseevable munths).

4 Eight days out, the little fella was sircumsize. That age they don't mind so much.

5 Abie-ham was struttin' around, a 100-yeer-old new father.

6 But Sairy thot, "Everyone who

heers about this will laff. Who'd a thunk I'd be milkin' at my age? There's a suckler borne every minit."

8 When I-sick got weened, Abie-ham threw him a coming-off party.

9 Hagger brung her boy Ish-male, who had a nice time playing with little I-sick.

10 Sairy got sore, wispered to Abie-ham, "Git them outa here. I don't want our sun-and-air mixed up with that little blowstairs kitchen-basterd."

11 Abie-ham was upset too.

12 God sed, "Stop fussin. I-sick is yer rite-full hair but I plan to do all rite by Ish-male too."

14 But next morning Hagger was sent off with her boy, some bred, and a skinful of water into the be-wilderness.

15 She wandered off over Bare-she-bare way. That skinfull soon got drunk. What to do here in the wild-ness with a dry kid on yer hands? Hagger stowed him under a bush.

16 The kid started to cry.

17 God herd.

18 Told Hagger to git the kid up and he'd make him a grate nation.

19 All the little fella wanted was a drinka water. God sed, "Keep yer eyes open," and He made a well fer them both to git ther skinfull.

20 Ish-male staid on in the wildness and becuma kinda Nature-boy, livin by the sweat of his bow and arrer.

CHAPTER 22

Now it was time fer God to put Abie-ham to the test. But it looked more like I-sick's final exam.

2 "Abie-ham!" "Here, God."

"Good. Take young I-sick up on the mounting and the two of you have a roast." "Sure, God. Roast what?" "Roast I-sick."

3 Not a peep outa Abie-ham. He riz up next mornin, got his ass sad-dled, and put on his boy I-sick. Took along two pair of hands to cut wood fer the barby-cue.

4 God pointed out the place for the roast, and Abie-ham got his weeny son reddy.

5 And he sed to the hired men, "In case we need more kindlin you two better split."

6 Then he lade the wood on his son I-sick, and went off up the mounting, with a knife in one hand and a fire in the other.

7 Haff way there, I-sick felt ther was somethin missin. "Father, we got wood and we got fire, but where's the little roast lamb?"

8 Abie-ham swallered and sed, "God pervides."

9 When they was both on the spot, Abie-ham bilt a alter, loded it with wood, then, as he was bound to do, tyed up his son.

10 Now comes the knife part. (Fer-git about the burnt offyring.) Abie-ham riz his hand, "This is gonna hurt me worsen you."

11 Down dove a Lord's Angel screaming, "Abie-ham!" twice.

12 "Spare the child and save the fire. God jist wanted to find who was the boss."

13 Abie-ham lift up his eyes once agin, but he never got a chants to say a thing. Fer there was this old ram cot his horn in a thicket, and it end up in the holycost stedda the boy I-sick.

I-sick helps his dad with the barbycue

14 And that Angel sed, "Becuz you were reddy to put everything into this sackerfice inclooding yer son, God is gonna make sure that you and yer tribe never run outa sons agin. They will be as noomeruss as all that grit on the seeshore."

CHAPTER 23

I-sick's mother, Sairy, hung around fer 127 yeers, to see if he was gonna be all rite.

2 She finely packed it in at the old homested, over there in Cane-in Land, up Hebe-run-way.

3 Abie-ham hadda make the burry-all arrangemints with the lokel Hit-tites.

4 He sed, "I'm a non-Hit-tite myself, so kin I jist have a little someplace outa site, fer a plot?"

6 Yer hed Hit-tite seth, "Be our Guest. Caves is good fer what you want."

8 Abie-ham agreed. "How bout that cave, end of Eefrin's feeld? I'd pay full price."

11 But Eefrin wuden take a thing fer it. He give Abie-ham feeld, cave and all, unfurnisht, fer free.

13 Abie-ham insist, "At leest lemmy pay fer the feeld."

15 Eefrin ansered, "Lissen, what's a four-hunderd-sheckle feeld tween two peeple like us. Go ahed. Berry yore ded."

16 So the deel was close. Abie-ham give Eef the 400 sheckle.

17 Abie-ham got his feeld.

18 And Sairy got her cave, post-humorusly.

CHAPTER 24

Abie-ham was gittin on hisself. A widderer, he was more worried about his son, I-sick's martial status, than his own.

3 He sed to his hed fourman, "Put yer hand up under my rite thigh, and swear to me you'll never let my boy marry one of them lokel Canine girls. I want you to git him a nice back-home girl where we come from in Messup-a-dameyuh.

5 Sed the hired man, "But spose them back-home girls wants to jist stay back home? Mebby I should take the boy along, and if the girls see him in yer flesh, then how they gonna keep 'em down on the farm?"

6 But Abie-ham spake up, "I-sick stays where I can keep a eye on him.

7 God'll probly send a angel or two along with yuh to garntee delivery."

9 So the hed hired man swore all the wile puttin his hand under Abie-ham's thigh.

10 The he up and set out. Took along ten of the boss's camels, who took on considerbull water and the hole camel pool and took off fer Messup-a-dameyuh.

11 They hedded deep south. Outside city of Nayhoar (no frost) them camels got ther first drink in days. Lotsa wimmen about drawin' water wile the camels was drawin' flys.

14 The hed fourman thot here was a good place to find a well-brot up girl. But howdya find out? Thot the hired hed man to hisself, "If I ast a girl fer to gimme a drink and find when I finely git my face outen the dipper that she's awreddy watering my camels, you can't beet that kinda circle service for a wife."

15 Before he'd dun saying this, out

Rebbeker, a well brung-up girl

come, jarred to the shoulder, Rebekker, dotter of Beth-you-all, who was son by Nayhor out of Milk-a. (Jist by co-ingy-dingy Nayhor was one of Abie-ham's brothers, never removed.)

16 Altho' she'd bin a filler for quite some time, Rebekker was still yung and cumly, a vessel awaiting her made-in voyage.

17 When Abie-ham's man ast her fer a drink, she give him a jar.

19 Wile he was slurping, she offert to draw fer all them camels. She musta bin a quick draw.

20 Before he finisht gulpin the jar, she had humped enuff water fer all them ships of the dessert.

21 The hired man wundered if God's hand was on the pump.

22 After the water-in, the hired man paid Rebekker off with a gold ring weighing haff a sheckle, and a paira bracelits too. She ended up well sheckled.

23 Boldern brass, he ast the girl, "Hooze yer father, and has he gotta room fer me?"

25 Rebekker run down her famly tree in breef and sed she'd see if ther was hay and straw enuff fer anuther.

27 The hired man heeved a sigh of releef, "This must be the place, thank God."

28 Rebekker run home with her bracelits a-clankin to tell her brother Lay-bin.

30 Lay-bin took one look at all that joolery and yelled fer that hired man.

31 "Come in, come in, and brung yer camels, too."

32 The camels was brung in and un-girdled wile Lay-bin laid on straw, hay, and water fer foot-washin.

33 Then it was time to put on the feed-bag, but Abie-ham's hired man figgered it was show-and-tell time.

34-48 So he told, what you bin told.

49 After it was told, the hired man said, "But have I come too close fer cumfurt, ending up with a girl who is reely Abie-ham's neece?"

50 Lay-bin ansered, "God only knows. Take her and git."

51 So the hired man give out Abie-ham's presents ... gold, silver, raymint, and costly arnaments fer all the famly.

55 Lay-bin wanted to keep Rebekker around till she had matoored anuther ten days, but Abie-ham's man figgered he had made a big enuff deposit, and ast Rebekker if she had itchy feet.

56 Rebekker cudn't wait to brake the famly tyes. By the way, she brung her nurse with her.

60 Lay-bin let her go sayin, "May all yer trubbles be thousands of little ones."

61 Rebekker, nurse and hed hired man got up on ther high camels and strode out of Lay-bin's rooms.

62 Meenwile back at Abie-ham's, I-sick was far-out in the back dessert, meddletating. Then he seen the camels are coming.

64 When Rebekker clap eyes on I-sick, she got down offa that camel.

65 Bein shy, she covered herself with a big vale.

67 I-sick took her home to his hills anyways, vale and all.

CHAPTER 25

Fer his part, Abie-ham wasn't finished yet. He tuck anuther wife and she bore him sons till deth at 175.

2-19 A list of them mite bore every-buddy to deth.

20 I-sick was jist passin forty when he took Rebekker. She turned out like his mother Sairy, absolootly barn.

21 I-sick prayed for Rebekker to be delivered of this barn condishun, and Rebekker conseeved twins, so his wish had bin grunt.

22 But the wife coodn't deliver, fur the two little feet-usses kep argewin' over who had first place even in the woom. The muther-to-be thot, "If this's the way it's gonna go on, let's quit rite now. What's the point?"

23 But God sed, "Try to be simble-minded. You got two nations in ther strivin agin eech other. One strong, one weak, and I'll give yer a hint, yer older will end up waitin' on yer younger." (What elts is new?)

24 Rebekker finely had her comin-out party. A dubble Bill.

25 First one out was all red-denhairy. I-sick called him Eesaw.

26 Last but not leest, holdin' on by his brother's heel, come little Jake-up. Anybuddy who kin git started with a heel of a brother has got somethin going fer him.

27 They sure grew up differnt, them two. Eesaw was a wildcat and a hunter. Jake-up was a barn cat, more of yer gatherer. One lived wild, the other intents.

28 I-sick lean-to his boy Eesaw becuz he was always game, out fer it,

and would bring him back some. Jake-up was his momma's boy.

29 Wile Eesaw lernt to hunt, Jake-up lernt to cook.

30 Once he was biling up some porridge, and Eesaw come in, ravitched, coulda eat the jam off the door, and he yelled, "What'd you bake, Jake? Gimme sum!"

31 Jake-up sed, "Trade you some fer yer berth-rites."

32 Eesaw sed what did he care about rites or lefts, he was rorin hungry.

33 But Jake-up made him sine fer the hot stuff first. Eesaw was in sich a hurry he dip his pen twice in yer roled oats.

34 And that's how come Eesaw sold his berthmark fer a mess of porridge.

CHAPTER 26

Famin time come agin. Jist like yer dirty thirty dust-bole.

2 I-sick thot of cuttin out as fer as Ejippt. God sed, "Don't go. This land is yer land, and I owe it to you to fix it up fer you and yurn, on accounta yer father was my best man."

6 So I-sick stuck pritty close to home, movin a short hop to where his father used to homested, among yer Fillasteins.

3 Them Fillasteins could be ruff customers, and Rebekker was still pritty fare to look upon, so like father, like son, I-sick dun the same trick with his wife Rebekker, "Keep smilin and tell them yer my sister."

8 Nobuddy minded this fer a time, till King A-bim-a-leg, yer hed Fillastein, saw I-sick fondling what

he thot was the fella's own sister. A-bim-a-leg sed, "Now I know why yer called I-sick."

9 When he finely found out I-sick had bin fondling his own wife, A-bim-a-leg sed, "What is it with you peeple?"

10 I-sick sed that his famly never liked to take chantses with ther good-lookin wimmen.

11 "No," sez A-bim-a-leg, "you let us take all the chantses, and then God help us if we git cot gittin fresh." And he put the No Tresses Passing sine on Rebekker, and fer good mezzure, I-sick too.

12 I-sick dun good among yer Fillasteins.

13 He becum downrite rich.

14 After a time, them Fillasteins becum jellus.

15 They filld in all the wells that old Abie-ham had dug up yeers ago.

16 If that wasn't a big enuff hint, King A-bim-a-leg come rite out and sed, "Move on. Yer gittin' too big fer yer breaches."

17 I-sick moved to a further-out vally. Father Abie-ham had bin ther before, so I-sick spent his time witching fer water and digging out them old wells of his fathers.

19 When he struck water, I-sick struck trubble with yer lokel herdsmen, who were Drys, but not by choice.

20 The more they complaned, the more wells I-sick dug. He called all them holes by differnt names, but it was nothin to the names he got called.

23 He finely ended up Bare-she-bare way.

24 God sed, "I'm here, so don't you worry."

25 I-sick bilt a alter, pitched a tent, and dug anuther well.

26 King A-bim-a-leg, who was not a well man, come over to see him. He brung along his army hed, who was Phicol.

27 Sez I-sick, "What are you two standing around here fer when it's me you can't stand?"

28 "Fergit all that," they sed, "you've got something we ain't got, which is water, so we'd like to git in on this cuvvinant arrangemint you started with yer Lord."

29 What they reely wanted was a testy-moanial frum I-sick and a letter of reckmendation to God.

30 So they all swore oafs at eech other and celibated with a party.

31 The morning after, they swore some more and went on ther way.

32 I-sick's servints went out and dug another well, proving all's well that brings up another one.

CHAPTER 27

When I-sick got reely old, his mind was still sharp, but his eyes was a bit dim. Sumtimes he dint even know his Eesaw from a hole in the ground.

2 One day he sed to Eesaw, "My son, I may be old and dim, but there's nothing wrong with my taist buds.

3 Git yer bow and arrers, go out and git yer old man some country meat.

4 I'm still game fer a wild cut of sumthing that moves fast thru the bush."

5 Wife Rebekker overheerd this, and grabbed her number one son, Jake-up.

6 She watched Eesaw hit the bush, then tole Jake-up, "Now's yer chants.

9 Go out to yer father's flock and git me a coupla good kids. I'll game them up kinda spicy.

10 Then you bring it to yer ole man with his blessing. Oh, and jist pertend yer yer hick brother."

11 "It's a neet idee," sez Jake-up, "but how kin a smoothie like me pass off as my hairier sibbuling?

12 One feel of my fourarms and I'll be left outa Dad's will, without a if, and, or butt to stand on."

13 "There's a way where there's a will," smiled his mother.

14 So into old I-sick they brung a little lamb drest up in wild rice.

15 Rebekker drest Jake-up too. In Eesaw's old cloze.

16 Last but not leest, she cuvvered his neckin hands with skins from some old gote.

18 Jake-up walks in with more gall than a canal horse, and sez, "Come'n git it, Dad, by cracky." "Who's that?" sez sick old I-sick. "Yer first out, Eesaw," sez sneeky Jake. "Here's the game I brung you."

19 I-sick was at first susspishus. "Pritty quick huntin, warn't it?"

20 "The Lord helps them as helps therselves. So dig in."

22 "Funny, you don't sound like him. Lemme feel yer, Eesaw . . . Well sir, isn't that hairy. The sound is Jake-up but the feel is Eesaw."

23 Old I-sick never knew hide ner hair of what he was groping.

25 But he sure et and drunk up a storm.

26 He was so tickled with that meal he wanted to kiss his boy. When Jake-up come near, in the borried close, old I-sick felt only Eesaw could smell like that.

27 "That's my boy!" And he give Jake-up Eesaw's blessing all the wile cursing everybuddy else.

30 Jake-up saw Eesaw comin' acrost the barnyard, so he snuck out.

31 "Well, Paw, time to put on the feedbag!"

32 "Who're you???" "Number one son."

33 I-sick got the shakes. "I jist bin stuffed by him. And give him my blessing too. He gits the blessed of everything."

34 Eesaw let out one ring-tailed snorter of a great howl when he realized he'd bin gulled by the other boy. He minded the time he sold his sole fer a mess of pot-hash.

35 "Bless my sole, father, ya got enny left fer me?" "Sorry son, too late. Yer brother has the gile, so yer left with the bile. He's lord of the bunkhouse and yer at bottom of the pay-roll."

36 Eesaw sniffed and sed, "You must have sumthin' in yer stockin fer me!"

37 I-sick thunk hard. "Well yer not gonna be one of the fat livin offa the land, and yer few frum hevven will be a longtime a-coming. Yer gonna have to live by yer sord and work fer yer nex-of-kin . . . but the day'll come when you break this yoke over yer neck."

41 "I'druther break little Jakey's neck rite now," grunt Eesaw, "and then the yoke'd be on him."

42 He meant it too. He pland to kill him off the morning after old I-sick bot it. Eether then, or the next time he had a good fit, whichever come first.

43 Rebekker got wind of this on the party line, and she tole her little pet it was time to pull up his tents and steal away.

44 "Stay with my brother Lay-bin's folks till Eesaw's wind dies down."

46 I-sick was tole the reason little Jake-up was going to visit the in-laws, was on accounta his mother dint want him carrying on and marrying up with any of them Hit-tight hussies.

CHAPTER 28

I-sick agreed. He tole Jake-up to find hisself a nice, homey Heb-rewed girl. So Jake-up was packed off to his in-laws over to Pad-in-a-ram, where his mother Rebekker's brother homestedded.

11 On the way, he stopt off to sleep one nite, and all he had was rocks for his bed. He made a pillar out of one and slept on it. And did he ever dreem.

12 He dreemed that angels was going up and down all nite on a kinda esky-later up to Hevven. Up at the top was God Hisself who called down to Jake-up that he would make the same pact with him He dun with I-sick and Abie-ham. Jake-up was smart enuff to agree.

18 He got up and pored oil on that stone what had bin his piller, and called it Bethyl, which means House of God, which is a good start.

19 Jake-up figgered on giving God ten purrsent of all he made, as his part of the bargin.

CHAPTER 29

Jake-up hit out eest, and come to a well with a big bolder on top of it. Around it was sheeps waitin to be watered.

9 So was Raycherl, dotter of Lay-bin, who was brother of Rebekker, who was mother of Jake-up. Jake-up musta bin a bit of a mussel-man becuz he roll back that bolder like it was a pebbil, so Raycherl got her flock watered.

10 When Jake-up found out Raycherl was his kissin' cuzzin he wep fur joy, then kist her.

12 She run and tole her father who came runnin' and there was a lot more kinkissin.

13 Jake-up staid a munth.

15 Finely Lay-bin sed, "Why don't you work fer me? What kinda wages you want?"

16 Jake-up jist sed, "I want Raycherl."

17 Lay-bin sed, "Fine. Seven yeers." He also had a weak-eyed older girl name of Leeyuh, but no menshun was made of her in the deel.

21 Well sir, seven yeer went by, and time for Lay-bin to pay off.

22 Ther was a wedding feest, and the bride was all a-cover-up (like they did in them days).

23 She even kept the vale on thru the hunnymoon nite. And the next morning Jake-up found out he had wed weak-eyes Leeyuh. (His own eyes coodna bin too good eether, vale or no vale.)

Jake-up makin sheepish eyes at Raycherl

24 Natcherly he complaned to Lay-bin, who clamed that yer older stribling has to be unloded before yer yunger, and then had the gall to tell Jake-up he cud have Raycherl if he hung around another seven yeers.
25 Jake-up bot it. On accounta he only had to wait a week to git Raycherl into wed-lock. (Biggerme was common in law in them days.)
26 Still it took Jake-up seven yeers to git rid of his det to Lay-bin, as well as two mouths to feed and no children to speak of.
27 Later, the Lord saw to it that Leeyuh bore sons wile Raycherl was still barn. When it come to sons, it was Leeyuh 4, Raycherl 0.

CHAPTER 30

Raycherl complaned to Jake-up, who sed, "Don't lookit me, fer God's sake."
3 She got so desprit fer sons she sent her maid Bilhaw in to Jake-up to bare fer her.
4 It worked. Bilhaw come up with little Dan. Jake-up was so pleezed he tride it agin. Worked agin.
5 Leeyuh got in on this too. She give Jake-up her maid Zilpaw. So along come little Gad. Follered next by lil' Asher.
6 Seems everybuddy got into the son bisness. Leeyuh started baring agin, and God took it all back so that Raycherl started too. By the time Jake-up was finished his part, he got hisself a baker's dozen, twelve sons and a dotter, Diner.
25 Jake-up figgered it was time to git back home, after all the service he dun fer Lay-bin.

26 Lay-bin, he know the Lord was oney on his side as long as Jake-up hung round and dint want him to go.
27 But Jake-up was homesick fer to show off all his famly to the old folks at home, I-sick and Rebekker.
28 When it come to divide up yer sheep and yer gotes, Jake-up made it eezy fer Lay-bin. He sed, "Jist gimme the gotes with spots on them, and I'll take all the black sheep in yer famly too."
29 Lay-bin thot that was gittin off eezy, speshully when he tole his sons to git all the freckled ones to a far-out pastyer, takin the black ones on the lam with them as well.
30 Jake-up was left with the rest, which mounted to nuthin on accounta every one of them was spotless. But he was never spot-out-a-luck, our Jake-up, he cud give it to Lay-bin in spades. It was matin' time among yer sheep and yer gotes, and most of that happened around the old waterin hole. So Jake-up he peeled poplar rods till they had white streeks in them, and stuck 'em up in front of them ruttin' and drinkin' aminals. He seprated yer lambs frum yer gotes and set them to breed among the rods so that all ther offspring would come out like them rods, with spots on 'em. That way, Jake-up cleend up total on the new crop, and Lay-bin was sheep-outa-luck, and Jake-up got his gotes too.

CHAPTER 31

Lay-bin was a sore loser, and so was his sons.

34

2 But his dotters Raycherl and Leeyuh they was on Jake-up's side, and felt like forners. They was reddy to hit the trail anytime.

3 Raycherl was so fed up with father she stuck all of his household gods in her trunk.

4 Jake-up deesided to flee wile Lay-bin was sheering his sheep. They got acrost the You-fraidies river before Lay-bin cot up with them, hard by Gilly-Ad.

5 "Why did you sneek my dotters off without so much as a farewell kiss? I was all set fer to give yez a send-off party with tamberines and liars."

32 That's what Lay-bin sed when he overtake Jake-up and company. "You know Jake-up, you are my son-in-law, everything I have is yores, sept possibly my household gods, and by the way who's got-tem?"

33 Jake-up didn't know about Raycherl's shopliftin. He tole Lay-bin to serch ennywheres.

34 Lay-bin went thru a in-tents serch. Raycherl she had tuk and stuck them gods under a camel saddle. And sat on the camel herself fer to make sure. As Lay-bin went by her on the hump she excused herself fer not gittin' up as she warnt too well, that time of the munth being come.

36 Lay-bin found hyde ner hare of nothing. So Jake-up let him have it. Not the gods, which he dint know about, but twenny yeer of frustera-tion in the in-law bizness, forteen gittin' two of his dotters (one of which he didn't want) and six yeer gitting a few sheep with spots on

them. And that's about all Jake-up had to shofer, on accounta Lay-bin paid him whatever he had a mind to, and changed his mind at leest ten times.

37 When Lay-bin saw that he was beet, the krafty old devil deesided to make up with Jake-up.

46 So Jake-up sed, "Since you've made a heep outa me, git together a heep of stones and we'll call it Quits." (But insted they called it Mizzpah, which is a kinda benny-diction which meens: 'May the Lord watch over you and me, when we are absent one frum the other. And you stay on yer side of the heep and I'll stay on mine and we'll git along jist fine.')

47 After that they had a party and ate bred all nite, and in the mornin' both partys hit out fer home in opposit direckshuns.

CHAPTER 32

To Jake-up comin' home meant meetin up with his brother Eesaw. That cud be a bad thing, if Eesaw had the mammery of a ellaf-unt.

2 Jake-up sent out feelers fer to find out if his brother was still mad at him. He got nerviss when he herd his brother was comin to meet him and bringin with him four hunderd other men. Sounded like a possy.

7 So Jake-up divide up his flocks, sheep, gotes, wife, kids and camels into two groops, so that if his brother was reely mad cleer throo, Jake-up still mite git by with a loss of fifty purrsent.

9 He also reminded God of his

promises, like making all his dissendents like the sands of the sea (which is to say noomerous, rather than washed up).

13 He also sent on ahed lotsa presents to his brother Eesaw, naimly two hunderd yous, forty cow, ten bull, twenny ram, thirty milky camels pluss ther hairy camel-colts, plus I dunno how many she-and-he-asses. All this Jake-up figgered might make him accept-a-bull in Eesaw's eyes.

22 That nite he sent the wife-maid-sons-and-dotter part of his outfit ahed acrost a stream.

24 Jake-up staid aloan, and had a ruff nite. Sumbuddy was rassling with him until daybroke. But Jake-up was tuff . . . he dint know what it was he was rassling, but he warnt gonna give him two fall outa three.

25 The other fella saw he cuden beet Jake-up, so he pull Jake-up's thigh outa joint. This was jist as day was braking, not to menshun his hip.

26 But Jake-up dint give in. He held this stranger in a haff-nelson sayin', "Bless my sole, I won't let go till you do!"

28 The stranger turned out to be a rassler called The Angel, and he sed, "Yer name is Jake-up no more. You have bin face to face with yer Maker, and frum now on yer called Izzreal fer you have pre-veiled over both God and men."

32 And that's why to this day Izzrealites won't eat that part of the thigh-bone on anything, since that's the part where God cot Jake-up, jist there on the holler by the sin-you of the hip.

CHAPTER 33

Eesaw he was comin on jist the same, and the 400 was with him. Jake-up took no chantses. He put the maids in front, Leeyuh and her brood in the middle, and Raycherl with lil Joesiff, his yungest, in the reer. Then Jake-up stood up in front of his brother and hit his forehed on the ground seven times 'thout bending his knees.

4 Eesaw fell on his neck. Not his own, but Jake-up's, and end up kissing him like a long lost brother, which he was. Everybuddy breethed eezy.

11 Eesaw dint even want all those presents. But Jake-up was so fulla gilt frum before about the hairy arms that he made sure this time he treet his brother with kid gluvs. So Eesaw kep all them he-and-she beests.

12 And he was so tickled, he wanted to light out fer home that minit, and bring Jake-up and kin along with him.

13 But Jake-up dint want to truss his luck too far. He tole Eesaw he cuden keep up with him, on accounta all Jake-up's kids, both them in the flocks what was still on the tit, and the young tads of his'n that hadn't bin weening too long neether.

14 So Eesaw went back home, and Jake-up moseyed along jist a short ways and set up shop in Succoth and stalled there with all his cattle. This was hard by yer city of Sheckem which was inhibited by yer Hivites. To make it legal Jake-up bot the land from them before he made his pitch with his tent.

CHAPTER 34

Diner was Jake-up's only dotter (out of Leeyuh, you'll mind), and she paid a call on her new naybers.

2 Well sir, young Sheckem, the local prince, he took a fantsy to her. (And took was the word, without so much as a by-yer-leave.)

4 Mind you, it was love at first grab. He ast his old man Hammor fer to git him Diner fer his wife.

5 When Jake-up first herd about this, he was aloan. So he waited till all his sons come back from the feeld. They was pritty riled up about ther kid sister.

6 But Sheckem's father come to Jake-up first fer to Hammor out a deel.

8 He was all smiles, wanted to be frends, and relativs too. Promised big weddin presents too. And more weddins between ther two tribes.

13 But Jake-up's boys figgered ther sister had been defiled as well as defloured, on accounta Sheckem wasn't sircumsize. They was sore about it, and they wanted others to be sore too.

14 They wanted Sheckem's hole outfit done that way.

25 But Jake-up's boys was out fer blood. Three days after all of them operations, two of Jake-up's boys, Levi and Simian, done a little operation of ther own. They swoop down on Sheckem City unawears, grabbed Diner back agin, sloo all the males, and plundered off ther females plus cattels and chattels.

30 Jake-up he was fit to be tyed. "What kinda welcum waggin is this among these forners who out-nummer us?"

31 All the boys cud anser was, "Wood you like yer sister to be treeted like a harlet?" Nobuddy ast Diner what she thunk.

CHAPTER 35

God spoke up. "Git back to Bethel where you dreemed about that stareway to Hevven in the first place."

2 Jake-up tole his famly to git rid of them forn idols they bin packin' under ther camel saddles, and take the rings outa ther eers too, and hi-tail it back to home tairtory, where there was a alter to the one God who lookcd after them.

3 Jake-up rounded up all them rings and burried them under a oak tree out Sheckem way. Then he made plans to lite out before he and his got burried somewheres.

4 He thot he'd be pursood by all them other tribes lived roundyb-outs, but God whipped up a reel tairor that fell upon all ther citys, so that there was nobuddy left to chase after them. That'd be yer rath of God.

5 God reminded Jake-up his name warnt that any more, but Izzreal and to git on with the work started by Abie-ham and I-sick, bilding a land and having deesendence.

6 His wife Raycherl perduced a son, Benjammin, but it was hard labor, and she never come out of it. Jake-up set up a pillar on her grave and suddenly he dint wanta live there no more.

22 He pitched his tent over further by his father's. Old I-sick was now a

hunderd and eighty, and pritty much in the shade. He finely died old and fulla daze.

CHAPTER 36

E esaw lived over to Edom among dissendents too numerous to menshun.

CHAPTER 37

J ake-up dwelled over to his father's place, in Cane-in.

2 His faverit son of them all was Joesiff. He even got him a speshul uneyform fer to stand out frum all the rest.

3 His brothers dint take to that too much.

5 Joesiff was a big dreemer. And he loved to show and tell. This dint go down too good neether, speshully when he had dreems like they was all stooking in the feelds, and everybuddy's stook fell down sept Joesiff's.

6 But it reely took the cake when Joesiff dremt the sun, moon and leven stars bent over backerds to bow down to him.

10 Even his father purt neer rebuked.

14 Joesiff was pritty much a home-boy but one day old Jake-up sent him out to his big brothers who was afar puttin' out with ther flocks.

19 When they seen him comin' they all sed, "Here comes this dreemer, whyn't we kill him and see what he dreems then?"

21 But the oldest, big Rube, sed, "Let's not be bloody about this. I know our little brother is the pits, so why not jist throw him in one?"

23 By the time Joesiff cum close, his fate was seeled. First they dun a strip of his fantsy-cullered bath-robe, ripped it up the back, then he was cast in the star part at the bottom of a pit.

25 Along cum a buncha camels baring some Middy-nite traiders hustling gum, bom and murr down Ejippt way.

26 Brother Judy spoke up, "What good is it to leeve our own kin and bone down in the pits, when we kin sell our flesh fur a profet?"

29 Rube he was somewears elts at the time and when he got back yer pit was bare. He thot the wurst of his brothers and they never tole him what reely happent.

31 They kilt off one of ther gotes, and dipt Joesiff's cote in gote blud.

34 When Jake-up seen that torn bloody thing, he rip up his own garmints. They tole him his pet was rented to peeces by a wiled beest. He wooden talk to none of them fer days.

36 Them Middy-nites hit Ejippt and sole Joesiff down the Nile to the hed of Faro's gards, Pottyfur.

CHAPTER 38

T hings went even worse at Jake-up's place. Judy, he had married a Canin-ite and she give him two sons, Err, and O-nan.

2 Err he was give in mirrage to Tamar, but nothin happend. The Lord got so fed up with Err, he sloo him.

8 So Judy sed to O-nan, "You gotta do the rite thing by yer sistern-law. Go in and raze up some off-spring."

9 Now O-nan was a purrverse

Joesiff gits in the famly way again

bird. He figgered them offsprungs wood never be his so he refuse to take issyuh with his ded brother's bride. Insted, this bird spilt his seed on the ground. That O-nan was in a class by hisself, and the Lord sloo him too.

11 Tamar, the widder, sez to her father-in-law, Judy, "Well, what'll we do now?" And Judy sez to Tamar, "Wait'll my yungest boy Shelah grows up." (They dint bleeve in looking round too much, them Izzyrealites.)

12 When Judy's wife past on, he was in the same fix as Tamar. But she dun sumthin' about it. She tuk off her widder's weeds and put on the vale of a harlet, wated by the rodeside fer her father-in-law to come along frum sheer-sheeping.

15 Judy saw her sittin' ther like Kurb Service and figgered he'd buy.

16 First come the price.

17 Judy sed he'd give her a kid frum his flock. Tamar she wanted some coldlateral first. Judy end up leaving with her his signalet ring, his staff and his cord, so there'd be sum strings attatched.

18 After they got to know eech other, as they say in this Good Book, Judy he went off fer to find that kid fer paymint.

19 When he come back, she warnt there. Judy ast, "Where's the harlet keeps her beet rite by the rodeside about here?"

20 The other fellers sed, "That was no harlet, that was yer dotter-in-law."

21 It wernt three months before Tamar was back, biggern ever. With Judy's child on the way.

27 Judy had a full flush, admit he was the Daddy and wated fer the delivery date. Turned out twins.

CHAPTER 39

Meenwile, back in Ejippt, Jake-ups's faverit boy Joesiff was gittin' along jist grate. Fer a slave.

2 His boss, Pottyfur, was pritty bizzy with all of Faro's gards which he was in charge of, so he made Joesiff seer over everything elts round the home.

6 Now Joesiff had growed up to be quite a looker. He dint need no striped cote fer to be took note of by the ladies.

7 Mizziz Pottyfur she was lyin' round doin nothin wile her huzbin was playin Gards, and as well as the rest of the house she wanted Joesiff to be over her too.

8 But Joesiff figgered his master had give him enuff in hand, and he dint want to take on the added wate.

10 But Miz Pottyfur kep on hinting that it wernt too much of a burdin fer her to bare.

11 One day, on the maid's day off, she up and grab Joesiff by the cloke, and order him to stop making the bed and pay attenshun to her.

12 Joesiff he jist checked his cloke with her and run off.

13 All Miz Pottyfur got fer her pains was a peece of tairy-cloth.

14 But that was enuff to make trubble fer Joesiff.

16 When Mr. Pottyfur come home, she made up a story fer him out of this hole cloth.

18 She clame Joesiff made the first move, and when she screem alarms,

his last move was to flee the house.
19 Well, Pottyfur warnt too pleased at having a snake in the house, so Joesiff he end up in the hoosegow.
21 Even there he dun well. Throw the boy in a dunghill, and everthin' still cum up rozes.
22 He becum like his Keeper's brother. Soon he was in charge of everything in jail sept the keys. He was over all the other prizners, and the Jailkeeper he jist sat all day playin Solitairy.

CHAPTER 40

Joesiff was soon join by other extingwished cumpny.
2 Faro got teed off with both his cheef butler and baker, and put them both in custardy.
3 Joesiff's job was to wate on them. The butler sure dint mind that. Him and the baker loafed all day.
4 At nite, tho' they was both trubbled with dreems.
5 Joesiff took care of that too. He tole them he'd tell them what there dreems meant, as soon as they wood reel them off.
9 First Joesiff found out what the butler saw. "I seen this vine with three branches, and there was buds on them branches, and before you knew it there was blossoms, and all of a sudden, bang! there was yer grapes! So I took them grapes and squoze them into Faro's cup, and give the cup to Faro, now what's that meen?"
12 Joesiff sed, "I don't do reedings. God duz 'em. But here's what He sez. You take yer three branches,

that's reely three days in the life of a butler. Naimly, the next three days. That's how long it'll be before yer back at the old job, helpin Faro in his cups."
13 The butler started reechin in his pocket, but Joesiff sed, "Jist remember me when yer back on the job, and Faro needs a spair servint."
14 Then the baker rise up and sed, "What about me? I dremp I had three hampers of cakes on my hed, but the birds was eetin' all the cookys outa the top basket, and them was sposed to be fer Faro."
18 Joesiff gulped and sed, "You hadda go and ast. Them three baskets is three days, and that's how long it'll be before Faro lifts up yer hed, but this time yer body won't come with it, on accounta yer gonna hang frum a tree, and them birds will be eetin' yer cookys."
20 Three days later it was Faro's berfday and he give a party fer all his servints. And serprize, serprize, he lifted up both yer hed butler and yer hed baker. Yer butler was back servin cups, and yer baker was hung over a tree.
21 And what about Joesiff? Did the butler remember who figgered out his dreem? If you think so, you must be a dreemer.

CHAPTER 41

That butler fergot fer two hole yeers. It warnt till Faro started havin dreems.
2 Faro sed, "Whew! What a nite! I dremt seven big fat cows come outa yer Nile and et grass. Then seven skinny cows come outa the same river, took one look at them fat

cows, and et em all up. Now, what kinda deel is that?"

3 When Faro finely got back to sleep, up come another nite-mare. This time he got seven plump eers of grain groan on the one stalk. Nuthin wrong with that. But then after that come seven thin eers, with the blite on them, and they swallered up the seven good eers. Faro felt that was kinda goin agin the grain, so he ast all his Cort Magishuns to come up with something fer an explanashun. But if them Magishuns knew anything, they kept it under ther top hat.

9 Finely the butler minded Joesiff still back in the callerboosh, how he scored hunderd purrsent when it come to dreems.

14 So Faro orderd Joesiff disinturd and brung before him, to disinturpert his dreems.

16 Joesiff sed it was up to God, not him, to come up with the ansers.

17 So Faro tole him about the fat heffers et up by the skinny ones, and even after doin that kinda canninball thing, they was still as skinny as before. Joesiff was all eers, so Faro tole him his other dreem about the stocks of corn, thin eers swallerin' fat ones.

25 Joesiff told Faro the two dreems was the same one. Seven eers is seven yeers and so is yer seven cows. And the eatin' part jist ment seven yearsa plenty follered by seven of fammin, when everybuddy will be frum hunger.

32 The fack that Faro had the same bad dreem twicet, jist meant that God meant it in spaids.

33 Joesiff tole Faro he better git

sumbuddy in charge knows what he's doin.

34 Faro sed to Joesiff, "You seem to know what yer talkin' about. What wud you do?"

35 Joesiff sed if he was Faro he'd set grate stores aside and be pritty reserve about his food for the next forteen yeers.

36 Faro deesided to set grate store by Joesiff and pit him in charge of this food program as yer cheef Overseer.

41 So Faro set him up over all Ejippt. Sept the throne, which Faro kept fer hisself.

42 But as fer the rest, nobuddy cud raise hand ner foot in Ejippt without Joesiff bein in the know.

45 And Faro set Joesiff up with a nice Memfiss girl and they made the hole thing legal.

46 Joesiff was thirty when he started workin fer Faro. Next seven yeers he was all over the place, hording grain fer the comin famin.

53 It come, too. In more lands than Ejippt lemme tell you. But thanks to Joesiff them Ejipptshuns had plenty of korn.

57 It got so the resta the world found out Ejippt was about the onley place to git bred.

CHAPTER 42

Meenwile back at the ole homested, Jake-up was startin' to wonder where his next crust was comin frum.

2 He sed to all his boys, "Don't jist sit there lookin' at eech others, git down to Ejippt and git us sum of

Joesiff tells Faro about his nashnul dreems

that cornbred, before we all throw in the towl."

3 Ten of them brothers got up off ther allotmints and hedded for Ejippt. Baby Ben he staid at home.

4 Wernt long before all them brothers was bowing their foreheds and scrapin ther knees in fronta ther long-lost brother.

5 It was like a dreem come true, becuz Joesiff minded who they were, altho' they dint' mind him at all.

6 He called them a buncha spys, jist fer to teeze them.

7 They tole Joesiff they were jist rude farm boys a long ways frum home, where ther father waited with his youngest fer to git sumthin in the bredbaskit.

15 Joesiff pertended he was sore as all git out, and tole them they better send a brother back home to bring that other brother back, and until he did, the rest of them brothers was to be held by Joesiff as hostidges.

17 And jist to show he ment it, he give them all three days in the clink.

22 Before they was took to ther sells, the oldest brother, Rube-in, started yanging at the others that this was ther punishmint fer doin' ther other brother in all them yeers ago when they threw him in the pit. Simian, he tole big Rube he didden know what he was talkin' about, on accounta he wasn't there at the time, and that pit-stop was oney about fifteen minits before they sold Joesiff fer export to Ejippt.

23 (They dun all this in the Yiddish, I spose, not knowing Joesiff cud talk ther lingo, him bein bilingamal in Ejippt.)

24 They probly wonderd why Joesiff was blowing his noze in the corner. But suddinly everybuddy was out on bail sept Simian, who was bound to go to jail till his brothers brung little Benny back.

25 Joesiff give orders to load ther asses with a full bag, and to tuck ther munny what they had brot, back in the sack.

26 First nite on the rode, one of the brothers got into his sack fer to feed his ass, and he see his munny back there on top. He tole his brothers and they was scairt purt neer to heart faleyure.

28 They all looked at eech other and sed, "Who in the name of God is doin this to us?"

29 But they never turn back the munny. They kep on goin till they hit old Jake-up's dorestep. Then tole him they had bin took fer spys, and they hadda leeve old Simian as a deeposset.

30 But that warnt the wurst part. Then they tole Jake-up that Simian was jist been held in truss until they imported to Ejippt little Benjammin.

36 Jake-up he was neer beside his-self. "You boys have breeved me outa Joesiff, Simian is out of it now, and yer gonna take away my lil Benny. What elts kin you do to me?"

35 That's when they all opened ther bags, and the munny fell outa eech one, and they reelized they got all that corn scotch-free.

37 So Big Rube sed, "That Ejipptshun Prime Minster is expeckin us back, and I garntee to return Simian and deeposit Benny fer yuh."

38 But Jake-up warnt havin nuthin of it. He figgered Simian fer ded, and dint want Benny to go the way of all that flesh. If anything happen to his youngest, Jake-up sed, his grey hares wood be all over the floor.

CHAPTER 43

B ut Jake-up change his toon soon after they et up the last eer of corn.

2 He figgered it was time to send sumbuddy to the store they had in Ejippt.

3 But brother Judy remind him, "We got a big brother in hock down there, and we gotta send up a little one in exchange. We won't git a look-in less we come up with Ben-jammin."

4 Jake-up was mad. "Big mouths! Why'd you tell him we had anuther one at home!!"

7 The brothers tole Jake-up that this fella seem to know all bout ther famly anyways, like he was gifted with the second site.

11 Jake-up thot mebbe they cud soffen up this hed Ejippt fella a little by taking him a few things on the side, like hunny, gum, murr, bom, awmends, and pisstasheo nuts.

12 "And give him his munny back frum the last time. Them Ejipptshuns loves munny I hear and when he give it back the last time it musta bin jist a Overseer's oversite."

15 They finely got off to Ejippt, Benny and all, and it warnt long before the hole she-bang stood in front of Joesiff.

16 When Joesiff saw his little baby brother, he orderd a animal slot-tered fer lunch.

18 The brothers was nerviss about goin to Joesiff's place becuz they figgered he was still sore about the munny that got into ther sacks, and mebbe he was gonna make slaves of them all and seeze ther asses.

19 Joesiff wasn't home yet, but his steward ansered the door, and ansered ther queerys too about that munny. He sed, "Joesiff got that munny the first time, so stop worryin, come on in and git yer feet washed."

24 They also had ther asses put up and given lots of hay.

26 Joesiff come home bout noon in time fer lunch, and the brothers was all waitin' shakin' in ther boots. Soon's he come in the door all ther foreheds hit the ground.

27 After Joesiff opened all his presents, gum, nuts, bom and murr, he ast about the old folks at home, naimly ther father. If he was well, or more to the point, still breethin.

28 They said, "Oh yes, Dad is still holdin up down there in Canin' Land.

29 Then Joesiff cot site of young Ben, his own brother by his own mother. And he had to turn away fer to turn off the teers.

30 When he give his face a good wash, he come outa the back kitchen and sed, "Soop's on!"

31 There was seprit tables. One fer Ejipptshuns and one for Heebrews, fer eech considerd the other a down-rite abdomination. Joesiff he sat with yer Ejipptshuns, but kept an eye on his Heebrew brood.

33 They was sat down in order of ther seniority, but little Benny, down at yer bottom, was give five

times as much to tuck away as any-buddy elts. He put it away, too. But nobuddy went hungry er thirsty.

CHAPTER 44

Joesiff give orders to his hired hands fer to load up his brothers' asses with corn and stick the munny they had alreddy give in on top agin.

2 "As fer little Benny, plant this here silver cup in his nappysack too."

5 Next mornin every brother was on his ass heddin fer home, when they was stopt by yer Ejippt hi-way patrole, who dun a rooteen serch, and found Joesiff's speshul cup where he dun all his reedings into the fewcher in Ben's bag.

7 The brothers was so upset this time that they all rented ther close, and went back to Joesiff who per-tended to be maddern all git-out.

8 Yelled Joesiff, "Whoever dun this cup-copping we'll find out by having a general dump-out. And if that happens to be yer bag, well yer the one gits to be my slave, and the rest of youse go on home!"

9 All them brothers knew it would be Ben had the missin silverwear. Sure enuff it clanked on the ground in fronta the baby of the batch.

10 Before Joesiff cud clame the boy, big brother Judy reered up and spoke, "Brother Benny shooda known bettern to try a thing like this with you and yer extry-sensual deception, but it'll kill the old man if he don't git back home on time. So put yer slave's bracelit on me insted."

11 "What's so speshul about Benny?" ast Joesiff.

12 Big Rube tole Joesiff that Ben was the only remainder son of Jake-up's favrit wife, Raycherl's other boy having bin lost in a pitfall sum time back, and morn likely tore to peeces by a wild untrain beest.

13 All the other brothers swallered hard, speshully little Benny, but Joesiff was havin' a fit inside. He tole all his Ejipptshun gests to hed home, and as soon as he was aloan with his brethren, he started bawlin fit to bust.

CHAPTER 45

Everybuddy was embarrased to teers by all of Joesiff's. Even them Ejipptshuns outside the door on ther way home herd the ruckus. Even Faro's householders cot wind of it, that's how loud was his carryin on.

3 But Joesiff dint care. He told the brothers to cum closer, and never mind the splash. He tole them he was ther brother Joesiff what they had sold down the river as fur as Ejippt.

5 They was all taken a step aback when they herd that, but Joesiff sed it musta bin all parta God's plan fer to keep the famly together with bred in ther mouths.

6 "It warnt you who put me down in Ejippt but Him Up There, and remember they's five yeer of fammin left to go, and I'm awful big in Ejippt so you better go back and git the old man, and everybuddy set-tle down at once rite here."

15 Then he fell on all the brothers' necks and kissed them, speshully Benjy's, and tole them to hurry up

Joesiff has a famly re-union

and bring down ther old Dad, and he'd git Faro to set 'em all up in a sub-divishun.

16 Faro, he was tickle pink to have Joesiff's famly move in on him.

18 He got them all loded and sent them back to Cane-in, promising them all that they wud eat fat offa the land.

19 "And take a coupla waggins fer yer little ones, and the little wimmen too, and don't fergit the old man. The best is none too good fer any kin of Joesiff's after all he dun." Thus spoke Faro.

20 Well, them sons of Izzyreal dint have to be ast twice. And the presents Faro sent along! More sheckles than you kin shake a stick at, Festeral garmints, ten asses absolootly loded with good things frum Ejippt, and ten she-asses the same way with bred and mix grains fer yer return jurny.

24 Last thing Joesiff sed to them was, "Come back in one peece. Don't fite on the way, fer God's sake."

25 No time at all seemed before they was back home.

26 Jake-up near drop when they tole him his number one boy Joesiff was alive and well and livin in Ejippt.

27 He sure revive tho' when he saw all them waggins Joesiff sent. Old Jake-up got carried away in stile.

28 All he was thinkin' as he left the old homested fer the last time was, "See Joesiff and die."

CHAPTER 46

On the way out Jake-up passed Bare-she-bare where he had had his own dreem of clime-in the ladder to excess.

2 God spoke to him agin, saying, "Don't be afrayed down there in Ejippt fer I'll still be with you-all and yer still going to be a grate nayshun."

3 There was a offal host of them lit out fer Ejippt tailin along after Jake-up. Regler waggin-trane it was. Sons, and sons' sons and sons' dotters, it wud take purt neers long to list 'em as it dun to git there. Anyways they was 70 in all.

28 Land o' Goshen! That's where they was all hedded.

29 Joesiff was there to meet them in his best charryit. When Jake-up come face to face with his boy Joesiff there was a raft of fallin on necks and kissin 'em, and tear after tear.

30 His father's greetin was tippical, "Now I know yer alive, I kin die in peece."

31 But Joesiff was more practickle. He tole his father and his brothers to tell Faro they was cattlemen, on accounta Ejipptshuns can't abide sheepherds, mebbe becuz they'd bin skinned too many times.

CHAPTER 47

When Faro met Joesiff's people he ast, "Whatta you do fer a living?"

4 Every one of them sed, "We're jista a buncha sheepherds."

5 But Faro counted on Joesiff so much, he dint seem to mind. But he tole Joesiff to see if they cud git a job handlin his cattle.

6 When Joesiff brung in his father Jake-up, Faro sed, "Well, bless my sole!" So Jake-up dun it fer him.

7 After that Faro ast Jake-up, "How ole are you?"

9 Jake-up sed back, "A hundert and thirty, and that's nuthin' cumpaired to my father and granfather!"

11 Faro was so pleezed to meet this long liver, he give him sum of the best land in the land of Ramseys (his own father).

12 Mind you, land ain't much during yer drout or famin.

14 There wernt much munny eether. It had all bin spent on food.

15 Even Ejipptshuns was broke, never mind them in Cane-in and points east.

16 When they all ast Joesiff fer food, he give them sum in exchange fer cattle.

18 Next yeer they cum back fer more food, there wernt no cattle to trade. So they traded therselfs.

19 Joesiff ended up buyin' all of Ejippt and all Ejipptshuns fer Faro.

20 The oney peeple he never soled into slavery was yer Preests, on accounta they all had allowances frum the Guvmint, and was fixed.

21 Joesiff's deel with the slave peeple of Ejippt was twenny purrsent discount. They kept four-fifths and Faro took the fifth.

22 Joesiff's own famly dun good out of it, and multyplyed till they was fulla froot. Old "see Joesiff and die" Jake-up was good fer anuther seventeen yeer.

29 At 147 he deesided to call it quits. He called in Joesiff and sed, "Promise me honor-brite (by puttin

yer hand under my thigh) that you'll take me back to the land of my fathers, and not burry me here on this lone dessert."

CHAPTER 48

Joesiff swore to do rite by the ole man, and brung along his own two sons fer to git granfather's blessing.

2 Jake-up was all bowed up to die, but he sat up in bed fer to look at his two haff-breed gransons.

3 Jake-up took one look and sed, "God Almitey!" He tole Joesiff of the Lord's promiss to give him and his deesendents the land of Izzyreal forevern'ever.

8 Now Joesiff's two sons was Eefrin and Manassuh. Jake-up cud hardly see them he was so dim with age in the eyes, but he wanted to bless them anyways, and bring them into the fold.

9 Jake-up took Eefrin on the one hand, and Manassuh on the other, and patted them both on the heds, crossing hands as he dun so.

14 That put the rite hand on Eefrin and the left on Manassuh.

15 This upset Joesiff becuz it ment he was givin' the back-hand to the first-born.

16 But Jake-up clame he knew what he was doin. "Young Manassuh will be grate, but his yung brother Eefrin is gonna be even grater."

17 Nobuddy spoke up at this point becuz the ole man was probly on his last leg.

18 Besides, last thing he dun was to deed Joesiff sum Canin' land Jake-

up had took by force frum sum Amourites with his sord and boa and arrer.

CHAPTER 49

After that, Jake-up brot all the sons in and called them names. Namely the twelve tribes of Izzreal. 29 And he charged them all too, to burry him in that cave where Abie-ham took Sairy and I-sick put in Rebekker and Jake-up hisself had already put away Leeyuh.
33 After Jake-up finished charging his sons, he breethed his last, and was gatherd in to his peeple.

CHAPTER 50

Joesiff took over the funerill. First cum the embombing which in Ejippt takes forty days. (The weeping fer him took 70.)
2 Faro was ast to let Joesiff make good his promiss.
3 Faro sent along a buncha elder frum Ejippt pluss charryit and horsemen making in all grate cumpny fer Joesiff and his famly on ther way back home.

4 After they buried ther father, Joesiff and all his brothers come back to Ejippt.
5 The brothers was still feerfull, in the pits of ther stummick, that Joesiff aimed to pay them all back fer what they dun to him, now that Dad was ded.
6 So they made up a messidge sayin', "Our father tole you to fer-give us before he died. Awrite?"
7 But Joesiff was still the ole sof-tie, and when they finely saw him, he wept agin.
8 His brothers offert to be his servints, but Joesiff sed, "Who'd you think I am, God?
9 You may have ment me evil, but God ment good, fer all of us, and our little uns too. So thank God yer here."
10 Joesiff stayed in Ejippt, live fer a hundert and ten yeer, dangled his granchildern on his nees, promissed his brothers that God wud sum day bring them back to the land of Abie-ham and I-sick and Jake-up. As fer Joesiff he was embombed and put in one of them Ejipptshun sarcoffa-gusses.

The Second Book of Moeziz, called

EXXODUST

CHAPTER 1

Joesiff was gone but that dint stop his dozen other brothers frum multyplying.

7 After a few jennerations the land of Ejippt seem to be fillt with them.
8 By that time they had a new Faro never herd of Joesiff. All he knew

was there was too many of his kind around. And if a war come whose side wud they all be on?

11 So he put them all to work on chane-gangs fer to bild him a lotta monyoumints. Sort of a Peer-amid Club. And club was what was used to make them all work.

12 But the harder they was worked, the more they was multyplying on the side, the more they spred abroad, till Faro got even more par-rynoid.

13 He made ther life even more fulla riggers, and hard ships.

15 Then he gotta new idee. Post-navel berth control.

16 He told all the Middlewives if they was tendin' a Heebrewer lady and she brung forth a girl, that was allrite, but if it was a boy, git rid of him rite off.

17 Yer averidge Middlewife they don't pay no mind to any man when there's a baby comin. Let him bile sum water or pace up and down outside.

18 Faro he called them all in and give 'em what for, fer letting all them he-Heebrews git born.

19 Them Middlewives tole him, "We never git a chants to see who is gittin' borned. Them Hebrood girls has awreddy had ther babees and finisht sweeping the floor before we git our noze in the door."

20 Good fer them Middlewives, thot God, and the Heebrew popilla-tion kep coming, male and female, both sides now.

21 Fer you take yer averidge Middlewife, she feers God morn enny Faro.

22 Then Faro got a new idee. Total immurshun till deth do its part. Every sunuva Heebrew born gits cast into yer Nile river.

CHAPTER 2

One woman from yer House of Leevighs got herself a good-lookin Heebrewed baby, and hid him fer three munths.

2 But word was gittin' around, so she figgered she better obey Faro.

3 So she cast him into the river, but with a little bull-rushy baskit fer to keep him aflote, which she dobbed with pitch afore pitchin it on the waters.

4 To make sure the little un was safe, the woman made her dotter, the baby's sister, be baby's sitter.

5 There was this little baskit bob-bin upandown among yer Reeds, when Faro's dotter cum down fer a dip.

6 She seen the baskit bobbin, sent one of her husky dusky maids fer to fetch it. Soons she seen what was in it, she sed, "Must be one of them little contryband Heebrews."

7 The little kid was cryin by now, so his young sister peered forth between yer bull's rushes and sed, "I know a good nerse cud look after that little tad. Works cheep."

8 Faro's dotter had alwaze wanted a son, but she warnt mareed and her father was picky-picky, so she thot, "Why not? Bring him back when he's weened. Meentime call him Moeziz."

9 So fer three munths little Moeziz was riz up by his own mother and babysat by Mirium his own sister. Nice famly arrangemint. With famly allowances comin in too.

Faro's dotter thinks Moeziz looks good in the rushes

11 Skip the next forty yeers. Moeziz was razed amung yer Ejippt types but never fergot he was one of them Hebroods. One day he seen one of his own kine gittin' beet by a Ejipptshun Overseer.

12 Moeziz fix that. He up and killed that Ejipptshun. Then he pertend it was all fun-and-games by burryin him in the sand.

13 Nex day he try to brake up a fight between two Heebrew. The one what had hit first sed to Moeziz, "Look who's settin' hisself up to be a jedge. Are you gonna knock me off like you dun that Ejipptshun?"

14 Moeziz figgered he shooda used more sand, and mebbe he better git outa Faro's way.

15 Faro was mad all rite. He sot Moeziz' life. Moeziz, he sot refuse amung yer Middlynites.

16 He got in a fight there too. The Middlynite preest had seven dotters and they went to the well fer ther sheepsake, but sum other sheepherds wooden let them have any water. Moeziz he got mad, and let them sheepherds have it with his fists, and wottered the dotters' flocks.

17 They was so tickled they tole ther ole man, the Hy Preest. And he invite Moeziz fer supper.

21 Moeziz staid fer morn supper. He end up with one of the dotters, Zipperuh.

22 He staid long enuff fer Zipperuh to bare a son, Gurshom, which meens "stranger in a strange land."

23 Moeziz was homesick, speshully when he herd old Faro had cash in his Cheops over to Ejippt. But the grone-in that was herd wasn't fer Faro. It was them Heebrews moanin over ther bond-edge.

24 God herd. It was time to keep the contrack with Abie-ham, I-sick and Jake-up.

CHAPTER 3

Moeziz he was still workin fer his fathern-law, Jeth Row, yer Middly-the-Nite preest. Moeziz kep his flock fer him wile Jeth Row look after the human flock, I spose.

2 One day, Moeziz was sheepwatching in the wildernest hard by Mount Sy Ny when he notissed a bush burnin outa control, but no ash comin outa it. Moeziz figgered he better investigate, how cum there was no ash out of all that burnin.

3 Now that God had cot Moeziz attenshun, He spoke to him from outen that blazin bush. "Moeziz! Moeziz!"

4 "Here!" sed Moeziz.

5 "Good," sez God. "Don't cum too close, but take yer shoes off on accounta yer standin on Holey ground." Which was true as of jist that momint.

6 "I am the God of all yer fathers, Abie-ham, I-sick and Jake-up." Moeziz was so scairt he run and hid.

7 But the Lord sot him out, to tell him, "My peeple is suffern in Ejippt, and it's time they was delivered. Time they moved on to a better place, fulla milkin honey, and I'm the Prime Mover, but yer gonna be the one to tell Faro."

11 Moeziz was vurry nerviss. "Who am I to stand up alone and tell Faro I'm taking all his cheep laber outa the country?"

12 God sed, "You won't be alone. Go and bring my peeple back here, and I'll tell you what to do next."

13 But Moeziz sed, "Do you think a buncha peeple are gonna hang around this here barn mountin jist becuz I say so? Who shall I say is givin the orders?"

14 God sed to tell them Heebrooze the God of ther fathers was behind all this.

15 "But," sez Moeziz, "I don't even know yer name!"

16. "I AM WHO I AM!" The bush fire blazed up for a minit. "Tell them the I AM has sent you on My behaff! Tell them to go three days into this wildernest, and make sac-krifices rite here." Moeziz frowned, "Faro mite have sumthin to say bout all this!"

20 God sed, "You leeve Faro to Me. After I stretch out My hand and smite Ejippt a few times, he'll be glad to let you go.

21 And don't go emmty neether. Bring not only yer jools, but yer nab-er's jools and close and put 'em on yer own sunsandotters. After our peeple leeve, them Ejipptshuns won't have a thing to put on."

CHAPTER 4

Moeziz was still nerviss. "Mebbe they won't bleeve me. Speshully when I tell them bout this bush that's burnin."

2 God sed, "What you got in yer hand rite now?" Moeziz looked and sed, "A rod. Why?"

3 God sed, "Cast it on the ground." So he dun it, and it turn into a snake. Moeziz jumped a mile.

4 The Lord brung him back, tole him to take it by the tail. Moeziz dun this and it straitened out into a rod agin.

5 "That'll show them who sent you," sed God. "Try stickin' yer hand inside yer boozem."

6 Moeziz dun this, and his hand cum out all lepperus snow-white.

7 "Put it back in," sed God, and the hand cum outa Moeziz's boozem normal agin.

8 "If you don't git them with the rod, the lepperus hand duz it every time."

9 God went on, "If all that don't work, take sum Nile water and pore it on dry ground. It'll change into blud. You can't beet blud fer changin' peeple's minds."

10 Moeziz was more nerviss now. "Even if I kin do these tricks, what kinda patter goes along with it? Fer one thing I stutter sumthin terribul. Even if I had the words, I cud never get 'em all out."

11 God sed, "Who made yer mouth in the first plaice? Jist remember, I'll be there with yer mouth when you speek."

12 But Moeziz sed, "Pleeze send sumbuddy eltse's mouth, Lord."

13 God got mad then. Moeziz had a brother, Erin, and figgered on sendin in a substitoot. But God was way ahed of him. "You tell yer brother Erin what we're doin, and he kin be yer mouthpeece, after you put the rite words in. He'll mouth what you tell him, which is what I tell you first, and when you go up in front of Faro, Erin'll work the mouth and you work the rod, plus the rest of the acts."

18 Moeziz was still shakin his hed when he got back to his father-in-law, Jeth Row's place. "I have to go check on my peeple over in Ejippt," he tole Jeth Row. "Go in peece, boy," sed ole Jeth Row.

19 And God sed, "Don't worry. All the Ejippt fellahs who were lookin fer you are now ded."

20 So Moeziz set his wife and sons on ther asses and they all went off Ejipptwards. Also the rod of God wuz in his hand.

21 God sed, "Mind you do all yer tricks before Faro but I wanna warn you, I plan to hardin his heart so's he won't let you go.

22 That meens you have to tell Faro that Izzyreal is My first-born Son, and when I say go that meens go . . . utherwise tell Faro to look out fer his first-born sons!" That's what God spaik.

27 God tole Erin to meet Moeziz in the wildernest. They kist and Moeziz tole his brother all what God had sed, and the bits with the rod and the hand and the blud.

28 Then both brothers started orgynizing ther elders.

29 Erin did the speeking and worked the sines this time.

31 That dun it. All them Izzyreal-ites bleeved and bowd down and worshipped.

CHAPTER 5

Then cum the big test in fronta Faro. "The Lord sez let His peeple go."

2 "Who He?" sez Faro. "I dunno Him. Whoever He is, I'm not lettin' no Heebrews go."

3 Moeziz and Erin sed back, "Bleeve us, He meens it. He wants jist three days in the wildernest fer His peeple. Or elts it's gonna be pestillents and the sord."

4 But Faro stuck to his guns (or whatever he used fer guns). "No three days off. Now all of you git back to work!"

5 And there was new rools fer the foremen in charge of Heebrews. "Don't give 'em enny more straws fer to make bricks with. Frum now on lettem git ther own straws. But make 'em make jist as menny bricks as was ther quoatuh before. An idol Heebrew is a cryin-to-God cumplaner. The only good Heebrew is a bizzy one. Keep 'em swettin."

6 After that every Heebrew was out snatchin' at straws tryna make a brick. This made it tuff on every-buddy, incloodin yer foremen in charge, fer they still had to make ther quoaters.

20 Them foremen tole Moeziz and Erin, "Thanks fer nuthin. That's what we have to make bricks with now, thanks to you two!"

22 Moeziz he turned back to God and sed, "What are we doin? I tole you not to send me! Everybuddy's still undelivered and worse offen before!"

CHAPTER 6

God sed rite back, "That was Faro's turn. Now it's Mine.

2 I garnteed the land of Cane-in to Abie-ham, I-sick and Jake-up and that still sticks.

8 Tell yer peeple I'll git them outa this fix and bring 'em back home."

9 Well, Moeziz tole them all that,

and do you think they'd lissen? They was too kow-towed down by them Ejipptshuns.

10 So God sed, "Moeziz, go tell the same thing to Faro."

11 Moeziz give a gulp and sed, "You meen when my own peeple won't lissen, I'm gonna git a heering frum Faro thru my lips that is both uncircumsize?"

CHAPTER 7

But the Lord charged Moeziz, and he give a charge to Erin too. So together they both charged on Faro. Moeziz he was 80 yeer old and Erin was 83 when they dun this.

2 God gave a few last instruckshuns, "When Faro sez proove it, pass a mirrorkill, then tell Erin to do the rod-into-snake act."

12 When they dun this in front of Faro, he call fer his own magic acts, and them Ejipptshun magishuns cum out and dun the same bit . . . the floor was jist fulla snakes what had bin rods.

13 No wunder Faro had a hardnin of his heart!

15 So God sed, "Wait till mornin when Faro takes his dip. Hang around the bank with yer rod and tell Faro if he don't let yer bunch go, you'll strike. Then strike the water with that rod and the hole Nile'll turn to blud. It'll choke the fish and nobuddy kin drink!"

20 Moeziz and Erin dun what the Lord sed. And it all worked. But Faro sed, "My boys kin do that too," and he turned round and went back home without his daily dip.

24 Meenwiles everybuddy was diggin round fer sumthin to drink, after the Lord struck the Nile.

CHAPTER 8

The water strike lasted fer seven days. Then God sed to Moeziz, "Time fer plaigs. If Faro don't let go, we'll plaig him with frogs. And I meen frogs in the bed chambers and frogs in the needing bowls; them Ejipptshuns is gonna be up to here in frogs."

6 So Erin strech out his hand with his rod over all the pools, puddels, all the water Ejippt had . . . even the land too, was frogcovert.

7 But them lokel Ejipptshuns dun the same thing, and brung on even more frogs.

8 That made Faro wanta call a halt. He called in Moeziz and Erin and sed, "Tell yer God to call off them frogs. Let my peeple go frog-free and I'll let yer peeple go."

9 Moeziz cuden bleeve his eers, but he smiled and sed, "Gimme 24 hour and you won't have a frog sept in the Nile."

12 Moeziz and Erin went back to report to God and tell Him to git on with the frog de-tale. God dun it. There was a heep of ded frogs every-wear and the land sure stank, but He dun it.

15 As soon as Faro was frog-cleer he change his mind about lettin go of yer Heebrews.

16 So God sed to Moeziz, "Time to give him the gnats. Jist git Erin to hit the dust with that rod, and that'll bug Faro all rite."

17 Erin struck dust and up cum them gnats. There wernt hide ner hare was free of them.

18 The lokel magick men tryed to cum up with more gnats, but they cuden. Mebbe ther heart wasn't in it, cuz them pesky gnats was everywears ennyways.

19 They tole Faro it was the finger of God what was doin it to them. Faro he musta had a muskeeter net, cuz he cudna cared less.

20 So God sed, "Jist wait'll old Faro goes out before brekkfuss fer his dip, and then put the flys to him. You and Erin pop flys into Ejippt. But don't worry about our bunch over to Goshen. There may be flys on Faro's fellahs but won't be no flys on us."

24 The Lord was as good as His word. It was fly-time in Ejippt and it roont it fer everybuddy.

25 Faro quit. He call in Moeziz and Erin and tole them to go sackerfice flys to ther God, and he'd give in.

26 But Moeziz sed, "What good will that do? If we go makin sackerfices and offerings they will be abdominabull to youse Ejipptshuns, and you will probly git us all stoned!

27 Let me git my peeple three days outa here somewears in the wildernest, and then we'll sackerfice proply, and you'll git rid of yer flys. But no goin' back on yer wurd, mind. Fare's fare, Faro!"

31 And God got the flys offa Ejippt, but that ole Faro he had hardening of the heart agin, and nobuddy got to go.

CHAPTER 9

God sed, "You tell Faro if he don't let go, we'll hit him where it hurts: in his cattel, his horse, his cow, his camel, his ass, and his flocksin herds. But don't worry about the Kosher cows, they'll be all rite."

5 Tomorra was to be the time. Moeziz and Erik sinkronized ther sun-diles.

6 Tomorra it was. Ejippt was fulla ded cows. You had to go over to the Heebrews fer to find a live one.

7 Faro musta bin a vegetaryarian, becuz he dint give a darn about all them ded beests.

8 So God call in Moeziz and Erin, "Time fer the ashes and dust bit. Grab yerself a handfull outa the kiln, Moeziz, and water fer to throw up in fronta Faro.

9 That'll put a fine dust over alla Ejippt and raise some boyles on everybuddy in site, man or beest."

10 They dun it, and the hole of Ejippt was sores afterwurds.

11 The magishuns of Ejippt cuden even bend down to try it they were so fulla boyles.

12 Faro he musta had offal soft cushions, becuz them boyles dint bother him none.

13 God sed, "Time to do a meddly of all the plaigs we have give Faro so far. And tell him I cud have cut him and his'n all off before if I'da mind to. Startin' tomorrow it'll be hale the size of billyard balls.

19 And member to bring the Kosher cattel in frum the feelds, or they'll git braned."

20 Them as feered the word of the Lord dun this, and them paid no mind, left ther stock out.

22 And God sed, "Strech out yer hand, Moeziz, and let 'er go!"

23 Moeziz put out his hand and you never seen sich thunderin' hale

and fire too, flashin' in the midst of yer hale.

25 That hale knock everythin in Ejippt flat. But over to Goshen, everything was cam and bammy. Yer flax and yer barly was roont, but yer weet wernt too bad, on accounta it hadden cum up yet. Musta bin winter weet. But everythin' elts was pound under.

27 Faro musta got knock fer a loop, cuz he call in Moeziz and Erin. "Awrite, awrite, get the hale outa here, and yer peeple too."

29 Moeziz sed, "As soon as our gang reeches the suberbs, I'll strech out my hands agin, and God will stop thunderin' and hale-in."

30 Moeziz shooda known better but he went out into yer Faro's subdivishuns and strech out his hand, and it was farewethers agin.

31 But soon as she stopped hale-in, Faro got hard-hearted agin. No hale, no deel.

CHAPTER 10

God sed, "Tell Faro I have jist bin playin' up to now. I bin hardnin' his heart on purpuss, so that I kin reely show who's Boss."

2 So Moeziz and Erin drug therselves back to Faro and sed, "How menny times you wanna do this? Startin' tomorrow it's gonna be locusses. Them things'll eet up what's leff after yer hale. And they'll move in on you like yer in-laws never dun."

7 Faro's servints was gittin tired of cleenin' up after all these plaigs, and sed, "How long you gonna keep this fellah Moeziz around. Lettim go,

Boss, he's more trubblen he's worth. Ejippt is flat on it's back on accounta him and that brother of his."

8 So Faro brung back Erin and Moeziz one more time. He sed, "Awrite, who of youse wants to go?"

9 Moeziz sed, "Jist the young and the old, plus ther sunsandotters and flocksin herds, that's all."

10 Faro frown and sed, "Jist the men kin go. If the hole she-bang leeves you must have sumthin' evil in mind." And he driv them out.

12 So God sed to Moeziz, "Turn on the locusses and lettem eet."

13 Moeziz wave his rod and brung up a eest wind, and that was what brung the locusses in.

15 That seem to pritty well cover things, them locusses. And they et ther way all thru Ejippt till there was nothin left but dessert.

16 Faro practickly cum runnin after Moeziz 'n Erin. "Fergiv me jist this oncet, fer I have sin, only git yer God to git these insecks offa my back!"

19 Moeziz sed he wud see what he cud do. And God sent a wesswind which bloo all them bugs into yer Red Sea.

20 But Faro's heart harden up agin and nobuddy got to go.

21 Then the Lord sed, "Strech out yer hand tord Hevven and there'll be a three-day blackout over Ejippt." Moeziz dun it, and nobuddy in Ejippt saw hide ner hare of eech other fer three days, on accounta they thot it was still nite and nobuddy got up.

22 But all was lite and brite over to

Moeziz shows Faro a bolt or two

Goshen, so Faro sed, "Go, git outa here, and take yer peeple with youse, oney leeve yer flocks in herds."

23 Moeziz sed, "We need them aminals fer to make burnt offerings. And we need our cattel too. Can't leeve a hoove behind."

24 Faro's heart seeze up agin. He was mad too. "Git outa here Moeziz, I doan wanna see that face of yers in here ever agin! Next time you see my face you die!"

25 Sed Moeziz, "Have it yer own way. I kin miss not seein yer face agin."

CHAPTER 11

G od sed to Moeziz, "One more time. That's it. This time Faro's gonna let go compleatly."

2 First, Moeziz was to go gather all the silver and gold jools frum everybuddy's nabers.

3 And they still thot enuff of Moeziz, them Heebrews, fer to dig down and give in.

4 Moeziz tole Faro, "Long bout midnite God is gonna go fourth mung yer Ejipptshuns, and look out fer yer first-borne, incloodin' yers, Faro. And that goes fer yer cattel's first-borne too. And you won't bleeve the wale that'll cum up outen yer peeple then.

7 But fer our parts, us Heebrews won't have a dog growl agin us. Then you'll kick us all out fer shure."

8 Moeziz left Faro fit to bust he was so mad.

9 With God tellin him all the wile, "Faro won't lissen. I've give him hardnin of the heart agin."

CHAPTER 12

B ut to Moeziz and Erin, God sed, "Here's my plan. Now we reely start.

3 You tell all yer congergations on the tenth of the munth fer to git therselfs a lamb. That's one lamb to a house.

4 If a famly can't manidge a hole lamb, let them split it with the bunch next door. Figger it out accorn to how much you kin eet.

5 But it better be good lamb. No spots. About a yeer old male. After that I don't care if it's frum a sheep er a gote.

6 Keep it till the foreteenth. That nite, everybuddy has lamb fer supper.

7 But don't waste the blud. Paint it on yer doreposts, eether side, and up acrost the top if you got sum left over.

8 The menu fer that nite is roast lamb, with unlevvyd bred, and herbs has to be bitter. That's the way it has to be et. It's no good raw, er biled with water eether.

9 Don't undercook it, er use too much water. And don't throw nuthing away. . . . Put it on the fire, its hed with its laigs, and all the other little bits too.

10 And I don't wanta see any lamb next mornin. What you can't eat, burn.

11 And eat as if you was on the run. Shooze on, loins girdled, and yer staff on hand, and eat fast. This is My Passover.

12 Fer I'm gonna pass over Ejippt this nite, and smite them in the firstborne, man and beest. And I will

fix a jedgement on them Ejippt gods too, bein Who I am.

13 Make sure about yer bloody doreposts now, fer when I see blud, I will pass over, and you won't be smit like them Ejippshuns.

14 You won't fergit this day. You'll mark this one till Kingdom cum, and have the same kinda feest ferever.

15 You'll be eetin that unlevvied bred fer one week. First day you throws out yer yeest. Anybuddy gittin a rize outa ther bred that week is kick outa the tribe.

16 And no work. Sept in the kitchen ... fer you all gotta eat.

17 But nuthin fantsy. This is the feest that cellabates the day I brung you outa Ejippt. And don't you fergit it. Ever."

18 Thus spake God. And Moeziz knew he meant it.

21 He tole every Izzreelite to git sum lamb, and save the blud in a basin.

22 "Then dip sum hissop leefs in yer basin and strike it on yer lintel, and yer doreposts. And everybody stay home that nite.

23 Fer the Lord knows what is comin, and He wants you to be safe as howsiz, but only them as has blud on the veranda is gonna be safe.

26 Yeers frum now yer kids will probly say to you, what was all that about?

27 You tell them, the bred is flat and the lamb is bitter tonite, on accounta that's the way it wuz when the Lord Past Dover and save us frum yer Ejipptshuns."

28 Everybuddy dun what Moeziz tole them.

29 And sure as He made lil apples,

it all cum true. Alla yer firstborn was slane if it was Ejipptshun, and that inclood cattel, prizners in the dunjin, and Faro's oldest boy hisself.

30 God dint miss an unbluddied house. You never herd sich a yell as went up frum that hole land.

31 God tole Moeziz and Erin "Pack up and git, flocksinhurds an all. And don't fergit to bless Me."

33 The Ejipptshuns were shure ankshuss now fer to git rid of them Hebrooze, before it cum to yer secund and third borne, or mebby the pairnts therselfs.

34 And them Hebrooze took ther dough over ther shoulders, before it had a chance to rize.

35 But Moeziz tole them before they set off, fer to borry frum them Ejipptshuns, all kinds of gold and silver, jools and raymont.

36 You'd be sprized how reezonabull them Ejipptshuns were at lending them Hebrooze whatever they re-choired. FOOTNOTE: (It sez in the Good Book they spoiled them Ejipptshuns, but you'd a thot it was the tother way round.)

37 There was six hunnert thou of them children of Izz-real, but that incloods the men and wimen too.

38 But not the flocksin hurds, and bleeve me by now they had "borned" very much cattel.

39 And they et on the run, with all that flat bred.

40 All that haste musta seem kinda funny, to yer Hebrooze fer they had bin hard by Ejippt fer 430 yeer.

42 Musta bin a nite to remember, becuz it's remembered still, the nite they pass out and over frum Ejippt.

43 Even today everybuddy in a

Hebroo house marks what ther fourfathers went thru that nite.

44 But servints workin in the house fer pay, they git the nite off, unlessen they've bin sircumsize.

45 Otherwise, forners and hired help ain't in the family circle that nite.

46 Whatever is et, is et in one house. No carryin leftovers to the naybers. And no bones broke neether.

50 Fer that was the day God brung out the children of Izz-real, out of ther bond-edge in Ejippt, with nary a bone broke.

CHAPTER 13

Faro finely let them Hebroo peeple go, and good riddens, he probly thot.

18 God led them by yer Red Sea, insted of over by yer land of the Fillasteins even tho' they was neerer than that Red Sea. But yer Fillasteins was war-like, and yer Red Sea seem peeceful in comparaison.

19 Moeziz brung along the bones of Joesiff, like he had bin promist.

20 God He went on ahed fer to point the way to Moeziz. He becum a piller of cloud. But that oney worked by day so He becum a piller of fire by nite.

CHAPTER 14

The first nite they all camp in the wildernest, heddin' fer the Red Sea.

2 Moeziz figgered Faro wooden foller, on account who wants to live in a wilderdnest?

4 But God wuzzent too bizzy bein a piller of cloud and fire, day and nite, fer to harden up Faro's heart agin. He wanted them Ejippshuns fer to know who was Boss.

5 When Faro lernt all his cheep laber had fled, he forgot all about the firstborne. All them Ejippshuns sed, "What'll we do without our maids and butlers?"

6 So Faro rev up his charryit, and give orders to all them other Kyro Charry-it-drivers to git with him too.

8 Six hunnert of them waggins was lined up, and Faro give the signal to move off. He went rarin off high-handed after his Izzyrale-ite hired help, that had all skip off with Moeziz.

9 Walkers is slower than horses, and Faro's charryits soon cot up with them Hebroo campers by yer Red Sea.

10 Wen them Hebrooze seen Faro's dust a-cummin, they lift up ther eyes, and hands too, and were they ever sore afrayed.

11 They complained to Moeziz: "You wanta bury us here in the wildernest becuz ther's no graves in Ejippt?

12 Why dint you leeve us aloan, let us go back and work fer them Ejipptshun overlords. It's a better job than dying in the wildernest!"

13 Moeziz sed, "Sit still. Feer not. As fer them Ejipptshuns comin' on to you today, I tell ya you won't see them no more ferever.

14 God is gonna do our fightin for us."

15 But God sed, "Don't cum cryin to me. Get them people of yours up

offa ther encampmint and go forward." "Forward?" sez Moeziz. "That there's yer Red Sea ahed!"

16 God sed, "Have faith. Lift yer trusty rod and point it at the Sea, and divide it up amung yer people and let them go down the middle on the dry parts."

17 Moeziz sed, "All rite, but are you gonna hardin Faro's heart soze he'll foller us with all them charryits?"

18 God sed, "Yes, but bleeve Me, when I get thru with that Faro he'll know his Red Sea frum a hole in the ground."

19 God sed nuthin more, becuz he turn into a piller of cloud and stood betwcen yer Hebroo camp and yer Ejippt charryits. That way there wuz peece all nite, with God actin as yer Nomansland.

20 Ackshully only the Ejipptshuns was in the dark. The other side of that cloudy piller was fire, which beamed as a nite-lite fer yer Hebrooze.

21 This help Moeziz with his work, (which was strechin his hand out over yer Sea) and God brung up a strong nor'easter dryland between them two wallsa water.

22 As day donned, yer children of Izz-real paraded up this drywalk between the wet-walls on ther rite and ther left.

23 But it was day fer them Ejipptshuns too, and they cum tumblin after, charryits and all.

24 But God was on the mornin watch, and when He seen them Ejipptshuns charryateerin after His peeple, He clogged the wheels on

them vehickles soze it wud be hevvy goin, in the sand.

25 Sum of them smarter Ejippt fellahs told Faro: "Let's git outa this muck. Them Hebrooze got God on ther side."

26 But they never got the chanst. God tole Moeziz to stretch out his hand agin now that all them Hebrooze had made it acrost toll-free.

27 Moeziz dun this, and the back up walls of water filled in agin. Filled in them Ejipptshuns pritty good too, Faro, charryits and all. Nuthin left but bubbles.

CHAPTER 15

The peeple of Izz-real was fulla faith after Moeziz brung them outa yer Sea without nobuddy gittin wet. Three days later, they wuz trampin thru the dessert complanin' on accounta ther wuznt no water.

23 When they cum apon water, they cudden drink, it was so bidder.

24 Then they started murmurin agin Moeziz agin, sayin: "What's to drink?"

25 Moeziz took it to the Lord, and the Lord give him this bush, sayin': "Add water and stir." So Moeziz throo the bush in the water, swished around a bit, and low, it was sweet.

26 Everybuddy sop it up, and Moeziz sed, "If you do rite by God, He'll do it all fer you. He won't give you none of them plaigs He put upon them Ejipptshuns."

27 So they all set by them palm trees and drunk water and had a fine time.

CHAPTER 16

But Moeziz made them move on into yer wildernest of Sin, which lookt too bleek to ern that name.

2 They'd bin on the road now fur a munth and a haff, and that murmurin was startin agin.

3 A lot of them sed, "I'd druther have yer fleshpots of Ejippt than this Sin place. At leest we had bred back home, and here, we're all like to die frum dyet."

4 God sed to Moeziz, "They want bred, they'll git it, but not where they expeck it. Up, not down. And it's gonna be rashind.

5 "Six days a week bred'll cum tumblin outa the sky, but twicet as much on Saturdays on accounta nobuddy works Sundays."

6 Moeziz and Erin tole ther peeple waitin in the bred lines, "The stuff starts tonite about suppertime.

8 And not jist bred. Meat at nite, and bred fer breckfust.

9 Don't tell me the Lord don't lissen to yer murmurins."

10 And it cum to pass. By nitefall, yer Hebrooze camp was cuvvered with quale, which everrybuddy had fer supper.

14 Stufft with quale, yer Hebrooze slept wile a hevvy dew fell on them frum above.

15 When the dew melt, it leff small little ballsa stuff look like hore frost.

16 Yer Hebroo knew what it wuz. "It's Manner from Hevvin." Moeziz sed, "It's God's bred. Pick it up, but don't take morn you need."

17 And they all dun so, morer less.

18 Moeziz saw that it was give out equal. And no leftovers fer the mornin, no hordin' fer midnitesnax."

19 But thers allweez sum that tries to git around orders. They smuggled sum Manner under ther pillers, and by mornin it stank to high Hevvin. Wormy too.

22 Funny thing, on Saturdays, when twicet as much fell, it never got rotten all day Sunday.

23 That's becuz Moeziz made them bake er boyle a hole batch up so's it'd keep over yer weekend.

25 That took care of yer Sunday Manners.

27 But there's allways sum as don't wanna lissen. Sunday mornin brite and erly a bunch was out tryna ern ther daily bred, in a Manner of speakin'. But there was nuthin on the ground, but dirt.

28 God sed to Moeziz, "How long you peeple gonna dodge my laws?

29 I give everybuddy ther daily bred and Sunday off too."

30 Moeziz nod his hed, He like that Manner . . . taste a bit like a hunny wafer.

31 Mind you, they was to eat the stuff till they cum to inhibited land, which was on the boarders of Cane-in, and that was forty yeers off. That's a steddy diet of Manner.

CHAPTER 17

Moeziz finely brung his children of Izz-real outa yer wilderdnest of Sin, and they was all thirsty agin.

2 Moeziz got the blame, acorse. But he sed, "Why blame me, you musta dun sumthin wrong agin the Lord!"

3 They still sed, "Is this why you brung us outa Ejippt, fer to have us and our cattel's tongue hang out here?"

Onward and upward with Moeziz in the dessert

4 So Moeziz cryd to God sayin', "Waddle I do? These peeple is about reddy to git me stoned."

5 God sed, "What's the matter with yer trusty Rod? Hit out with it. Only make sure you hit a rock, and see what cums off it."

6 Moeziz dun this, in full site of all them elders standin around.

7 He oney took one hit, and water cum out. And Moeziz yelled out, "Is God with us er not!! Wash yer faith and repent!" Everybuddy was too bizzy drinkin' to anser.

8 Then Moeziz led his peeple to new territory, altho old in a way, becuz it belonged to dissendents of Esaw, that hairy brother who got tricked by his smoothie brother Jake-up. Esaw's tribe was callt A-Malachykites, and they dint like them Hebrooze hangin' round ther drinkin water oasis.

9 They was fit to fite. So Moeziz sed, to young Joshawa, who looked fittest of all to fite, "Git sum of our boys reddy, and I'll stand on top of that hill with God's rod in hand."

10 Joshawa dun this, and as long as Moeziz held up his rod, them A-Malachykites dint have a chants.

13 Joshawa beat them off with his sord and God's rod.

14 God sed, "This is jist the start of the finish of them A-Malachykites. Make a note of it, and a copy fer Joshawa."

15 Moeziz dun better than that. He bilt a Alter, celibatin' the fack that God had it in fer all ther enemys.

CHAPTER 18

Back in Ejippt, Moeziz father-in-lore, old Jethro, heard about the doins in the dessert. He still had Moeziz' wife, Zipperuh his dotter, on his hands.

2 And the two boys too, Gersh'em and Elly-eezer.

3 They all tuk off frum Ejippt fer to visit Moeziz.

7 Moeziz cum outa camp to meet them, and kist them and ast about ther welfair, of which there is none in Ejippt.

8 He tole them all that God had dun fer His peeple, quales, manner, et setterer.

10 Jethro was wunover. He sed: "I kin see that yer God is the one." And he burnt a offring, and Erin cum in the tent and they all brake bred with the in-laws.

13 Next day Jethro watch his sunnin-law, jedgin' peeple from morn till nite as they wated fer him in line-ups.

14 Jethro sed to Moeziz: "How cum yer sittin up here, and the rest of yer peeple is lined up in yer waitin room the hole day?"

15 Moeziz sed: "Becuz I'm the only gobetween they got with God.

16 Wen sumthin's the matter, they all cum to me, and I have to referee becuz I'm the one who knows what God wants."

17 Moeziz' father-in-law sed, "You've took on too much.

18 Who appinted you as a jedge? You can't even jedge fer yerself, let alone fer all them. Take my advice. Let God be ther jedge."

19 But Moeziz sed, "God won't talk to these peeple, sept thru me."

20 Jethro sed, "Well you gotta git rid of these long line-ups. And it turns out yer the bottle'sneck. You

gotta dallygate sum of yer auther-
ority.

22 You cant handle six hunnert
thou peeple a day. Divide thim up
into hunnerts, tens and fiftys even,
and put groop captins in charge of
eech. Take the load offa yerself."

24 Moeziz hark to what his in-law
sed.

25 Suddinly ther was almost as
menny cheefs as Injuns, but it shure
cut down the linin' ups.

26 Moeziz he still look after yer
hard cases.

27 After that, Moeziz let his in-laws
depart. Jethro, he homered back to
Ejippt.

CHAPTER 19

The children of Izz-real was in
ther third month when they cum
unto yer wilderdnest of Sye-Nye,
same place where Moeziz first seen
that burnt-bush that never got con-
soom.

2 Everybuddy pitch in and camps
beside that mountin.

3 Moeziz clum up to talk with
God.

4 God sed, "Yer peeple has seen,
what I dun fer them. After what I
dun to them Ejipptshuns, I bared
them on eegle's wings fer to bring
them here.

5 It's time I put out sumthin in
writin, so that yer peeple will know
what I expeck of them.

6 Fer eggsample, I expeck every
man to be his own preest, and
alltogether holey.

10 Tell yer peeple the next two days
to wash therselves, and the third day

I will cum down and appeer, in site
of them all.

11 But tell them not to go up my
mountin! They dassn't even touch
it.

12 If one finger touches them
stones the body that belongs to that
finger will be either stoned or shot
thru. They kin just cum up to the
mount, when the trumpet sounds."

14 And Moeziz went down, tole the
peeple to wash up.

15 Fer two days they cleaned everything up. Incloodin ther persnal
habits with ther wives.

16 The third day it was mizzerbull
weather, thunderin' lightening, and
you cooden see the top of the mountin fer a thick cloud, and outa that
cloud cum a trumpet-call. Everybuddy shook in ther Sunday boots.

17 And Moeziz brung them all out
fer to meet God, at the foota that
mountin.

18 There was a lotta smoke and
even fire comin' out the top. Everybuddy quaked, and so did the mountin quite a bit.

19 That trumpet bloo loudanlong.
Moeziz anserd it, and God's voice
tole Moeziz to "cum on up."

20 The Lord cum down as far as yer
top of yer Mount, and Moeziz clum
up that far too. They met eech other
haff way.

21 God sed, "Go down, Moeziz
and charge everybuddy. Charge
them not to brake-thru and look on
Me, or they'll all be pairishabulls.

22 That goze fer yer preests too."

23 Moeziz sez, "I awlreddy tole
them that what you tole me before.
They know that Yer outa bounds."

24 And God sed, "Take this all

down and give it to yer peeple."

CHAPTER 20

I am Lord God Amighty, and these are the Ten things I demand.

3 No God but me. (FOOTNOTE: He is not jist Chareman of the Board, He is It.)

4 No cravin' imedges, or Idle Dollatry.

7 No takin My name in vane.

8 Nothin' on Sundys allowed but the Sabbith. Six days on, one day off.

12 No sassin yer pairnts.

13 No killin.

14 No Adult foolin' around.

15 No stealin.

16 No brakin' oafs or lyin' in cort.

17 Hands off yer Naber's everything.

18 All the peeple herd at the bottom of the mountin was the blare of that trumpit and lotsa smoke and thundernlightnin.

19 They yelt up to Moeziz, "Tell us what He sed, becuz if He tells it to us strait, we'll all be ded."

20 Moeziz yelt back, "Feer not, God jist wants to make sure you know what Sin is. In "righting."

21 And Moeziz went back into the dark cloud while peeple moved back to give Them both room.

22 God sed, "I guess they know not to look Me in the face by now, Moeziz.

23 This oughta stop them little mettle gods they bin turnin out up to now. Silver and gold don't impress me one bit.

24 Jist make me a alter outa Erth, and the odd sheep er ox to be bernt on it, that's all I ask of you and yours.

25 If you cant find the Erth, and you have to do with stone, then jist nacheral formations, none of that hewing for me. That sorta thing pilloots it.

26 And no steps up to My alter eether. I wuden want anybuddy to show anythin they shoodent."

CHAPTER 21

Now heers sum more rools fer yer peeple," sed God.

24 "Eye fur eye, tooth fur tooth, hand fer hand, and foot fur foot.

25 Burn fer burn, woond fer woond, stripe fur stripe."

CHAPTER 23

In return fer all this," sed God, "I'll destroy all yer enemmys.

28 I'll send horenets fer to drive out the Hive-ites, the Canin' Ites, and the Hit-Tites.

29 I won't do it all at once, or it'll roon the crops.

30 But liddle by liddle I will drive 'em out until you peeple granually take over."

CHAPTER 24

Moeziz writ down all the words of the Lord. He was on that mountin take-in dicktayshun forty days and nites.

CHAPTER 25

All the while God was dicktatin how to bild His tabernackle, fer to keep His commandmints in.

CHAPTER 31

And when God finished com-mooning with Moeziz on Mount Sighnigh He give him two tablets of stone on wich the finger of God had writ His commandmints.

CHAPTER 32

Down below, peeple got tired of waitin on Moeziz. So they went up to his brother Erin and sed, "We don't think Moeziz is cummin back. We better make up our own gods."

2 And Erin he jist sed, "Why not? Brake off yer eerings frum the eers of yer wives, yer dotters or even yer sons and bring 'em to me."

4 This they dun, and Erin he grave a imedge of a moultin' caff, the kind like they used to worship hard by Ejippt.

5 And Erin bilt a alter fer that caff, and called a prayer meetin fer the next day.

6 Nex day everybuddy got up erly, burnt sum offrings in fronta that caff, sat down fer to eet and drink, then riz up to play.

7 God cud heer ther whoopin all the way up His mountin. He sed to Moeziz, "You better git down there fast.

8 One word frum me, and they do as they like. They are one kruppt bunch of stiffnecks.

9 You better git that paygin thing meltid down, before I wax hot and cremate the lot of them."

11 But Moeziz had a few things to say first. "Now Lord, take it eezy on yer peeple. Why bring them all the way outa Ejippt to reduce them to ashes?

12 Wooden Faro's fellahs say them Hebrooze God jist brung them outa our place, led them a song and dance in the desert fer to knock them off in the mountins? If you ast me, God, you shood turn frum yer rath and say yer sorry.

13 You mind you sed to Abie-ham, I-sick, and Jake-up (which you baptized Izz-real, member) that you wud multyply ther seeds till ther wernt as many stars in Hevvin, not to menshun giving them this land what you promised ferever."

14 And God sed, "Sorry, Moeziz, guess I was kind of hasty."

15 So Moeziz cum back down the mount after takin two tabblets, writ on both sides, the one and the tother.

16 What was writ was what had bin dicktated by God and grave by him on them tabblets.

17 Joshawa met him haff-way, and as they cum down they herd one ring-tailed snorter of a hullavabaloo.

18 Josh he thot it was mebby war, but as they cum closer down, terned out to be sum kinda sing-song.

19 When they got rite down to it, it were a wild party, with everyone stomping ther boots as well as singin roundybout this caff. Moeziz was mad fit to bust. He brake them two tabblets rite acrost his knee.

20 But that was nuthin compaired to what he dun to that caff. He give it one big push into the fire, and ground her up till she was powderd. Then he took all that caff-dust and strood it over the water, and made all them Izzrealites drink it fer sediment's sake.

Moeziz lays down the law

21 And Moeziz sed to Erin, "Who's in charge here, and if it's you, what in Gehenner is goin on??"

22 Erin sed, "Don't git yer wax hot, Moeziz, you know what peeple git like lyin around with nothin to do.

23 They expecked you back sooner, with a god they cud worship, and wen you dint cum, well, they figgered, any god is bettern none.

24 So we had a gold drive, and cast this heer caff fer the part."

25 Alluva suddin Moeziz notissed that everybuddy was dancin buck naked, which was the dress derangemints that Erin had made. He reely got blud in his eye.

26 And Moeziz shout out: "Who is on the Lord's side, line up over here!" And before long, there was a hole bunch of Leeveye's standin there.

27 And Moeziz was so mad he sed, "God is even maddern I am, He sez fer you all to put on yer sords, and go thru the camp end to endwize, and slay yer bruther, yer frend and yer nayber, not nessessairly in that order."

28 Well they dun it, and by the end of that day there wuz 3000 less campers.

29 And Moeziz sed, "Today you have dun the Lord's serviss, by donaitin a son and a bruther and the odd frend to his cozz."

30 Moeziz hadda report back to God, on his peeple's sin, and ast fergivness.

31 God sed, "Git them outa heer, to the place I set up fer them. I'll send a angel along as guide, becuz if I went down Myself, I'd throw a plaig on all of them."

CHAPTER 33

After Moeziz cum down, everybuddy stripped and tuk off alla ther ornamints.

7 Moeziz was so embairassed he took the Tabbernackle and moved it outa camp.

8 When Moeziz went in, everybuddy stood watchin at the door of ther tense.

9 Soon as Moeziz went in, a cloudy piller cum down and hoovered in the doorway of the Tabbernackle. That meant the Lord was talkin to Moeziz.

10 Everybuddy seen it frum ther tense flaps, and they riz up and worshipped.

11 Inside the cloud, God was speeking face to face to Moeziz like an old friend. Sept that God cud see Moeziz but Moeziz cuden see God.

12 So Moeziz sed, "Show me Yer Glory, please God."

19 God sed, "If you saw My face you wud die.

21 But cum over here by this rock.

22 Git here in the cleft of this rock, and Ile cuvver you with My hand as My Glory passes by.

23 And I'll give you one little blink, after I've gone by. You won't see My face, but you'll git a glimpse of My back parts."

CHAPTER 34

When Moeziz cum out of that Tabbernackle after talkin to

71

God, everybuddy minded how his face shone.

33 In fack it shone so much, the glare on Moeziz was so strong, he hadda put a veil on his face fer to talk to his own peeple.

CHAPTER 35

And Moeziz lade down the law once agin, and tole his tribes they hadda move on, but they hadda take the Tabbernackle with them.

10 Moeziz thot a portible Tabbernackle wud be more the ticket.

22 So everybuddy brung all the joolry they had stripped off therselves.

23 Plus bloo, purpull and scarlit linens, and a lotta skin from gotes, badjurrs and ramses.

CHAPTER 36

They brung so much Moeziz hadda tell'em to stop.

CHAPTER 39

It was a home-made Tabbernackle, dun by the children of Izzreal therselfs.

43 Moeziz he made sure it was dun to God's specifickayshuns.

CHAPTER 40

God soopervized the work gang hisself, as a piller of cloud by day and a piller of fire by nite. When the cloud moved up and off, it was time for them Izzrealights to be on the move agin, portible tabernackle and all.

The Third Book of Moeziz, called

LEVICKEDNESS

CHAPTER 11

God got consernt about the Hebrooze diet.

2 He tole them what to eat and what not to eat when it cum to beests.

3 If a beest parted its hoofs, and chood its cud at the same time, it was eddible.

4 But if it did jist one of them things, speshulizing in cud chooing or clove-hoofing alone, it was out.

5 You take yer rabbit, he chooze his cud, but he don't split his hooves. Sorry.

7 Yer pig has a clove hoof but he don't choo his cud. Durty.

9 Fish dishes. If they got fins and scails. Awright.

10 Annything elts in water is an abdominayshun.

13 Also keep off eegles, vulchers, ravins, nite hocks, owls big and small, swans, pellycans, storks, herrons, lapwings, bats, and even yer grand old osprey.

20 All fowls that creep on all fores, is out.

21 Flyin fowls on all fores is in.

22 Yer lowcusst, balled or other-

wize, beatles and grasshoppers is eddible and alowd.

23 But other creepy things is out.

29 No weezils, mice, turdles, ferts, lizzards, snales or moals, or shlameelyuns.

CHAPTER 18

God tole Moeziz a few more things to let His peeple know He wuz God.

3 After all the doins in the land of Ejippt and all the goins on in the land of Cane-in what they were cummin to, He figgered He better git the Law laid down agin.

6 "None of yew shall cum neer any of yer kin, peekin around to uncover ther nakednest.

7 That goze fer yer father, yer mother, yer sister, yer father's dotter, whether they are borne at home or abroad.

12 That goze fer yer father's sister, yer mother's sister, yer father's brother, yer dotter-in-law, yer brother's wife, hands off alla them.

18 Don't ever marry yer wife's sister, not durin her lifetime.

20 Don't cuvvet yer nayber's wife, and then uncuvver her.

21 Don't lie with a man like a woman, it's abdominayshun.

23 That incloods beests. Wimmen shooden even stand in fronta beests, with a thot of lyin down. That's jist confusin."

CHAPTER 19

"Don't be greedy when you harvist. Leeve a bit in the corner and don't be so picky over the gleenins.

10 Leeve a few grapes too. Don't skin off everythin. Thinka the poor stranger and the stranger poor.

13 Stop defroddin yer nayber. And don't keep yer hired man's wages over-nite. He cant spend it in the morning.

14 Don't curse at deff peeple or put rode-blocks in the way of yer blind.

15 Don't be parshel to yer poor, or gruvvel to yer grate. Jist do rite by everybuddy.

16 Don't go tattle-tailing up and down lettin' everybuddy know what yer nayber's bin up to.

17 Don't hate yer brother in yer heart. Take it eezy on yer nayber too.

18 In fack, love yer nayber, jist like yerself.

19 Don't let yer cattel make ther own arrangemints. Mix-ups don't work. Don't mix yer crops neether. Don't wear mix close neether. Linen and wool don't work together.

23 When yer plantin froot trees, don't eat that froot fer three yeers. Takes that time fer a tree to becum sircumsize.

24 After four yeers, jist give thanks.

25 Fifth yeer, go ahead and dig in.

26 Don't eat nuthin with blud in it. And never mind the witchycraft neether.

27 No bangs when yer cuttin' yer hair, and no snippy-snip with the beerd.

28 Don't make cut-ups of the ded, and no tat-too-in of the live ones eether."

The Fourth Book of Moeziz, called

NUMMERS

CHAPTER 10

They was three days off frum the mountin on the way to where they was promissed.

34 And the cloud of the Lord hungover them by day and like a piller on fire by nite. Whenever they set out, the cloud was took up, and when it cum down agin everybuddy stop and staid in ther tense.

CHAPTER 11

But peeple was still complaners, and God herd about it, bein direckly above them in a cloud. And God got mad. He got so mad, that cloud of smoke cot on fire, and birnt up a lotta Izzrealites in the far parts of the camp.

2 The peeple cud see that God was put out, so they ast Moeziz to pray that the fire be put out too.

4 But them as wernt bernt, got craven fer flesh agin. They had had it up to heer with that Manner.

5 They minded how they used to git fish, wich you don't find in no dessert, and mellins, and cukes, leaks, uniuns, and garlick wich they thot was the spice of life.

6 Now they was livin with a Manner to which they cud never becum accustom.

8 Every day they'd harvist it, and grind it, or morter it, and bake a cake. Tasted oily.

9 They cud count on Manner regler as the dew. That was the trubble with it.

10 The childern of Izzreal wud cry, not for it, but frum it. Moeziz herd ther tears and complaned to God.

11 "Dear God, why did you give me this job in the first place? I dint ask fer it.

12 You say these are my peeple. Did I conseeve alla them? Why shood I hafta carry them round in my boozem like a buncha sucking baybees, to git to the land of ther fathers?

13 What am I gonna anser all these peeple when they ask fer flesh? My own is gittin weery.

15 I'm bout reddy to pack it in. So do me in."

16 And God sed: "Yer overworked. Git me three scored and ten of yer eldest sittizens, the ones as is reely in charge, and bring them over to the Tabbernackle, and let them take ther stand there.

17 I will cum down and spred the burden offa you and around them, so you won't be alone.

18 And tell them to wash up fer tomorrer, becuz there's gonna be meat on the table.

19 And I don't mean fer one day or even over the weekend.

20 I meen ther's gonna be meat fer a munth, you'll have meat comin outa yer nostrils till you'll all screem to be vegetary Aryans."

21 Moeziz jist sed, "That's a lotta meat. Ther's six hundred thou of us.

22 Are you gonna have slade all our

hurds, to do it? Or drane all the fish outa yer Sea?"

23 God seem miffed. "Is God ever short-handit? You let me worry about supplize."

24 So Moeziz went out, rounded up 70 old elders and set them round the Tabbernackle.

25 God cum down in a cloud, took the spearits out of Moeziz, and past them around the groop, so's that they cud profitsigh without seesing, when the spearit mooved them.

26 But there's alweez yer gripers. And two of them elders was jist that, Ell-dad and Mee-dad.

27 They went round profitsighing all over the place, when they wasn't sposed to.

28 Joshawa tole Moeziz what they was up to, and to put the kerb on them.

29 But Moeziz sed, "You must be jellus, Josh. I wisht all my peeple were profits. I wisht the Lord wud spred his spearits all over every-buddy."

31 Nex day was windy, thanks to God, and quales flew in from the sea, more quales'n you cud shake a rod at. They piled up a day's journey on both sides of camp and a coupla cubebs high, so that everybuddy was up to here in quales.

32 Took peeple a day and a haff fer bringin in the quale. The final score was ten homers. (FOOTNOTE: Whatever that means it don't mean pidgins.)

33 Everybuddy chewed quale till they coodn't bump ther gums no more. Musta bin tuff, becuz nobuddy had ackshally die-gestit any, when God smote them all with

a plaig. All them cravin peeple dropt like ded ducks.

35 Everybuddy moved on pritty fast after that.

CHAPTER 12

Moeziz married a Ethee-why-open woman, and that's when he got in trouble with his sister Mirium and brother Erin.

2 They sed, "Who is Moeziz to be so high and mitey speekin only to God. We're famly and jist as good as him. God speaks to us, as well."

3 Moeziz wuda agreed, on accounta he was as meek as they cum reely.

4 God spoke up, tole Mirium, Moeziz and Erin to report after Tabbernackle.

5 He cum down in His cloud, called Mirium and Erin forth.

6 And He sed: "Now heer this. I make all the profits around heer. If there's gonna be enny vizzyins I deeside who has them.

8 Moeziz is my go-bee-tween, he's the one I talk mouth-to-mouth with no dubble-talk. So quit tryna get in the act."

10 The cloud took off, and alluva sudden sister Mirium becum white as snow, on accounta she was now a lepper.

11 Erin ast Moeziz to git God back and fergive them.

13 Good ole Moeziz dun this.

14 But God cum back and sed: "She otta be ashame of herself, even if her own father had spat her one in the face. Keep her outa bounds from camp seven days!"

15 Mirium dun seven days

75

detenshun outa bounds, and nobuddy moved on till she was brung back in the fold.

CHAPTER 13

Now they cum to the boarders of the land of Cane-in. Moeziz sent out spys to infiltrait and check out the lay of the land.

23 They brung back a buncha grapes took two men to carry it on a Pole.

24 Took 'em forty days to git back. Musta bin big grapes.

27 They tole Moeziz ther was milk and hunny too but they cooden carry it all.

28 But mebby the lokel peeple cud, becuz they looked as high as the walls round ther sitties, wich was about fourteen foot.

29 Old Cale-Ebb, he tole Moeziz to move rite in and take over, but them as had bin ther spying, sed: "Are you crazy? We cum up to ther neeze. In ther sights weer grass-hoppers."

CHAPTER 14

Everybuddy cryed all nite when they herd that.

2 After the cryin cum the murmu-rin. "What are we doin here? We cudda died nice in Ejippt. Better even in the wilderdnest!"

4 Sumbuddy started a Back-to-Ejippt movemint.

5 That made Moeziz and Erin fall flat on ther faces.

6 Joshawa and Cale-Ebb they both rent ther close.

7 Then they spoke up: "That land out there which we took so much trubble to cum to, is reel good land.

9 Don't worry about the peeple that is temper-airily occew-pieing it. Ther jist grist fer our mill. They got size. We got God."

10 But everybuddy was reddy to git them stoned. Till God appeer outa his cloud, fumin.

11 God sed to Moeziz, "How long do I put up with this bunch before they bleeve Me. How menny more sines they want strewn along the way?

12 I'm bout reddy to disinhairit the buncha them, and smite them all with a pest-a-lents."

13 But Moeziz sed, "Yer Ejippshuns will be glad to heer that.

14 And they'll tell it to them Cane-in-nites, how you stood over our peeple day and nite, cloud and fire

. . .

15 And finely kilt them all off as one man. That'll go down good.

16 Sints You wasn't able to bring them all in that land like Ya'd prom-isst, You got rid of the hole lot in the wilderdnest."

22 God thot, and sed, "Ten times now these peeple of yorn have not harkend to My voice. But I'll let them go this one more time.

23 But bleeve you Me, nun of them as started out shall ever git to see this promised land. That's what they git fer provokin Me.

24 Sept Cale-Ebb. He has anuther spearit, he kin cum in.

29 But everybuddy twenny an over, is outa luck.

30 Sept Joshawa. He's in too.

32 But not you Moeziz. Yer carcase stays heer.

33 And yer peeple what was known as the children of Izzreal will have to

rome around fer forty yeers in this wildernest, till they drops, one by one.

34 That way they'll all know My Breech of Promiss.

35 I meen it. I will do it to them shure.

36 As fer them spys you sent out, which cozzed all the mummurin agin God, they was strick by the plaig, ever one.

37 Sept Cale-Ebb and Joshawa."

38 There was grate mournin amung the peeple.

40 And they riz up erly and gat them on top of the mountin and sed: "Us sinners is reddy to get into that Promist Land."

41 Moeziz sed, "Who tole you to do that? You can't go battlin' without God on yer side!"

44 They went ennywaze, and got smote all to peeces by them Cane-in-Ites, and ended up ded and discomfitted.

CHAPTER 16

Then the peeple of Izzreel got revolting. Two hunnert and fifty pertesters tole Moeziz and Erin they had bin on the take fer too long.

4 Moeziz fell on his face agin when he herd this.

15 God knows he had not took even one ass fer his pains.

28 "The Lord sent me to do all this werk. I am not self-employd."

29 God dint say a thing, jist open up the erth and swallered all 250 hole as the ground cave-in under them.

41 Nex day there was more murmuring agin Moeziz and Erin, sayin that they killed the Lord's peeple.

42 Down come the Cloud fit to burn.

46 Moeziz told Erin to spred incenst around fer to make a-tonement.

47 Erin dun it, but to no avale. Fire cum out from the Cloud, consume 250 incenstakers.

49 Not only that, but a plaig cum down, knocked off fourteen thou, seven hundert more of them.

CHAPTER 17

God sed, "Time to teech them peeple anuther lesson.

2 Tell everybuddy to pack a rod and write ther father's name on it. That'd be twelve rod, one fer every house.

3 Tell them Leevyes to write Erin's name on ther rod.

4 Lay all them rods together in the Tabbernackle, and I'll pick one fer first prize. First prize is a buncha flours that'll cum outa that rod. That shood shut up them mur-murs."

5 Moeziz charged all his printses a rod apeece.

8 Nex day, in Tabbernackle, Erin's rod sprout buds, with awmond blossems, and nuts, too.

9 It was kept in the Tabbernackle as a token aginst all rebbles.

CHAPTER 20

Moeziz' sister, Mirium, died.

2 And there wuz no water agin.

3 Peeple still complaned about why they was brung all the way out here thursty.

8 God sed, "Time to git out the rod, and knock it on a rock."

9 Moeziz was so mad he wanted to spare the rod.

10 He sed: "Do I have to go thru this agin, fer a buncha rebbles?" Sayin' it like it was his own doins, not God's.

11 But he dun it, and the rod hit it off with the rock and splash, splash. Everybuddy and ther beest drunk.

12 And God thot, "I'm not gonna bring this bunch over Jordan neether. And that incloods Erin and Moeziz fer sure."

16 They moved on, and cum to a boarder sitty in the kingdum of Eetum.

17 They ast fer rite of way on the King's Hi-way . . . jist strait thru, no stoppin fer a drink.

18 But King Eetum sed: "Nuthin doin. All yule git from me is my sord!"

19 After he turn them away, they all turn away from him off somewhere's elts.

24 God was mad, speshully at Erin fer lettin Moeziz use his rod without givin' God credit.

25 Erin was took to the top of a mountin, stript, and died.

CHAPTER 21

King Arid, the Cane-a-nite herd that Izzreal was spying on him. He cum after them and took sum of them prizners.

2 Izzreal promist God if He wud deliver the Cane-In-Ites, they wud utterly destroy all ther sitties.

3 God dun it, and they dun it too. Cane-In was wiped out.

CHAPTER 22

Nex they took on King Bollock who was sore afrayed.

4 He figgered that if Izzreal licked him, they wud lick up everythin he owned too.

5 He sent a messager off to the best curser in his land, old Bail'em over to Peethore.

6 Tole him to "cum up to the cassel and put the curse on them Izzrealites before we are all smitten."

12 But God got to Bail'em first, and tole him not to have that curse.

13 So Bail'em tole Bollock: "I can't go fer God's sake."

17 Old Bollock offert Bail'em purt neer ennything he wanted fer to cum and curse.

18 Bail'em sed, "What good will all that do, if the Lord is agin me?"

20 But God sed, "Jist fer devillery, go on up there, but don't use no words but mine."

21 Bail'em riz up next mornin, got on his ass and went.

22 God got mad when he went even tho He tole Bail'em to.

23 God sent a Angel to stand in the way of Bail'em's ass, with his sord in his hand. Bail'em didn't see no Angel but his ass did, and did a quick turnoff into a field.

24 Bail'em smote his ass to git it back on the track.

25 The track led tween two narrer walls. The Angel stud in the way agin.

26 Bail'em's ass swerve to avoyed yer Angel and crush Bail'em's foot agin the wall.

27 Bail'em give a big yell, and smut his poor ass agin.

28 The Angel dun it a thurd time, in a place where that poor ass cud turn neether rite ner left. So it jist lay down with Bail'em kickin and

screemin underneeth, and flailin' with his staff at his ass on top.

28 God put words in that ass's mouth, and she sed, "What have I dun to you, Bail'em to deserve all this smitten?"

29 Bail'em ansered his ass back without thinkin who it was had spoke. "Becuz you bin makin fun of me, and if I had a sord you'd be a run'thru ass, lemme tell you."

30 And the ass sed, "Nay."

31 Then God let Bail'em in on it, so he seen the Angel standin over there by the way. And Bail'em bow down so low he fell flat on his face.

36 Bail'em went on to Bollock's palace, and he was took up to all the high places so that the uttermost parts of the peeple cud see him and vice versy.

The Fifth Book of Moeziz, called

DUE TO RUN ON ME.

CHAPTER 1

It cum to this pass first day of the munth in yer forty-ith yeer Moeziz called everybuddy up again.

6 "God sez we bin long enuff on the mount. Time to dismount and settel in across the river as promisst.

21 Don't be scairt. Go git it. God sed yew cud have it."

22 But sumbuddy sed, "Have you seen the size of them over there? Ther all biggern us and ther sitties is walled-up to high hevvin. We can't git over it."

37 Moeziz sighed and sed, "You don't bleeve me or yer God. That's why He won't let me go over there with you all. He is mad at me fer yer sakes.

39 That's why we bin wandrin around fer forty yeers, so's none of you what started out will git in, and yer lttle ones, all borne on the road will be the ones as gits in."

CHAPTER 2

This day I'll put the feer a God into yer ennemys, and you watch them get the shakes."

CHAPTER 3

Moeziz cummand Joshawa go over have a looksee, on accounta Moeziz was furbid.

CHAPTER 31

He tole Joshawa: "I am a hunnert and twenny yeers old today. No more cummin in and goin out fer me. You go on ahed. I'm gonna sleep with my fathers.

31 I jist know that after I'm ded, all you people will thurly kerrup yerselfs. And yer gonna be in fer it, fer sure."

CHAPTER 34

Moeziz went up the mountin fer the lastime.

2 He got a good vue of all that he wuz going to miss.

4 God was waitin on him. "This is the land promisst to Abie-ham, I-sick and Jake-up. What you see is all you get."

5 Moeziz died.

6 He got burreed. Nobuddy knows where.

7 He wuz 120 and not a thing wrong with him.

8 Everybuddy staid up fer a hole munth and wepped.

9 Joshawa was the boss now.

10 But nobuddy was like Moeziz. He knew his Maker face-to-face. Nobuddy elts so far cud of made that clame.

THE BOOK OF JOSHAWA

CHAPTER 1

But God kept in touch with Joshawa.

2 Tole him to git movin over Jordan way.

11 Tole him to git his people to pack a three-day lunch.

CHAPTER 2

Joshawa wuz smart. He sent out two spys first fer to check-out.

2 First thing they checkdout was a harlit name of Ray Hab. They put up at her place.

3 This was in the sitty of Jerryco. The lokel king herd about Ray Hab's cumpny, and sent out a serch warnt.

4 Ray Hab hid them spys up on the roof under the stocks of flacks all of which she had layed up there.

12 She dun a deel with them.

13 She wuz the sole sport of her famly, which was quite a few livin in the same house.

14 Them Izzrealites spys knew a good deel when they saw one.

15 She let them all down gently frum her winder with enuff rope.

18 They tole her, "Jist so we'll remember yer place, have sumthin scar-lit in the winder and you and yorn'll git off scotfree.

19 But outadoors is outa bounds. Stay home. Utherwise the blud will be on yer own hed. Enny blud spilt inside yer house is on us."

23 Them two spys got back and tole Joshawa it was all rite to move in.

24 And that all the inhibitants they was movin' in on, wud faint when they dun so.

CHAPTER 3

They picked a funny time fer the Harvist cross-over. Mebby they didn't know Jordan overflooze its banks every yeer cum harvist.

16 But God musta bin with them, on accounta all them waters got piled up in a heep, until all yer children of Izzreal passover hy and dry.

CHAPTER 4

When everybuddy was clean passover hard by Jerryco, God tole Joshawa to prepair fer war.

CHAPTER 5

But after wandrin in the wilderdnest fer forty yeers, most of ther fite-in men had been kilt off. Now they reely was the children of Izzreel.

7 So when God tole Joshawa fer to sharpin his knife, Joshawa reelized sumthin elts hadda be dun first.

8 Not enny of this new jennyration had bin sircumsize.

9 Took a bit of time to recooperate frum all that.

10 Meentimes all they had fer fud was old dry corn and unlevvied cakes.

12 Yer Manner what had fall-in frum Hevvin fer the past forty yeer, had bin cut-off the day they passover Jordan.

13 Joshawa he went up to Jerryco to look the place over but he cooden git past the wall around it. Sumbuddy sat on the wall with his sord up.

14 Joshawa look up and sed to this sordsman, "Are you fore or agin us?"

15 The fella with the sord jist sed, "Take yer shooze off in the presence of the Lord." Fer this wernt a fella, it were a Angel wavin his holey sord.

16 Joshawa fell flat on his face. He knew he hadda git reddy fer a Holey War.

CHAPTER 6

Jerryco was a open and shut case fer Joshawa. Mostly shut, on accounta that wall.

2 God sed, "Don't worry, Josh, you'll git around it. Seven times to be exack.

3 And don't be sneeky about it. Letem know yer there.

4 I want a hole trumpit seckshun of preests to have a blast every time you git around that Jerryco.

5 It's gonna be a six day blast."

6 Joshawa dint shake his hed, jist folleyed orders and kept a strait face.

10 But God dint say nuthin about shoutin, so Joshawa deesided therd be none of that, till there was sumthin to cheerabout

11 They dun all this miles-fer-millyuns fer six days.

14 Nuthin happen.

15 They deesided on one more time. Not jist one circum-interfeerints of the sitty, but they kept on till they had dun it seven time.

16 That was when Joshawa tole them to shout jist as them trump-iteers was about blew out.

20 That dun it, that shout at the last trump-it, knocked everybuddy in Jerryco down flat, incloodin Jerryco itself.

21 Oney thing left up was Ray Hab's red-lite-house, and she was brung out safe with all her kin fokes.

22 She musta bin the last strumpit becuz after that Jerryco was burnt to the ground. (FOOTNOTE: Didnt have too far to go, bean alreddy flattern a unlevvied pannedcake allreddy.)

CHAPTER 7

Everythin got burnt up sept yer mettles, and them Izzrealites collected a lotta brass, arn, silver and gold, all of which was to be ternover to God, under the preevius arrangemint. But sumbuddy allus

Jerryco has a big cum down

trys to be sneeky, and one fella, Ackin, was jist akin' to git his hands on sum of that stuff, so he kept it to hisself.

2 Meentimes, havin knock Jerryco flat, Joshawa was gittin reddy to go agin the nummer one town of yer Cane-in-nites, A-I.

3 His spys made ther advantsis and report back that it wud take only two or three thou men to knock off this A-I place.

4 That's what they tole him so that's what Joshawa sent.

5 But it was the Izzrealites what got knock flat, and they cum back chaste all the way frum the gates of A-I.

6 Joshawa reelized he was up agin yer A-ones, so he rent his close, dusted his hed, and dusted off them elders too, on accounta ther curridge had turnt to water.

7 Joshawa ast God if He had brung them all the way acrost that river fer to git beet up.

8 He figgered if his peeple was gonna turn ther backs on ther ennemys, then they wud go on gittin beet up.

9 God sed, "First of all, git up offa yer face.

10 Sumbuddy has sind. Not so much back-slidin, as back-holdin on the lewt you recuvvered frum the roons of Jerryco.

11 That's why you dint have a chants agin yer A-one troops, and backed off frum a fite.

12 You got a rot-in-to-the core apple in yer barl. Git him out."

14 So Joshawa call all yer twelve tribes to cum to ther sensus, and finely this feller Ackin cum cleen.

21 He had fansied a good-lookin Babyloanish dress, a coupla hunnert sheckles of silver, and a gold wedgie, and hid them under his tense flore.

22 The upshot of this hole thing, was all them things was dug up, and Ackin got stoned fer his panes.

23 They heeped the stones over him fer to teech him a lessen, and them rocks is still there lookin' over him.

CHAPTER 9

Now that they was in God's good Books agin, ther was nuthin stoppin them Izzrealites. They knocked off one tribe after anuther.

2 Sept fer a groop frum Gibby-un.

3 Them Gibby-uns wuz smarter than the rest.

4 They drest up in ther old close, climbed on their asses with old empty wine bottils, and moldy bred, and went over to see Joshawa, pertendin they had all cum frum a far country.

8 They tole Joshawa they was immigrunts, and was willin to take any job, however meanyell.

9 Joshawa look at ther moldy bred and empty bottils and figgerd they had cum as long a jurny as him and his Izzrealites had.

15 He figgered these Gibby-unnites was in the same boat as his peeple, so he let them in the same leeg.

16 But this trick dint last long. Took bout three days before Joshawa reelized he had bin had by a costoom prade, and that these Gibby-uns cum frum jist over the hill.

17 But a bargin is a bargin and Joshawa hadda stick by it. He was

stuck with these Gibby-uns and all ther funnin games.

21 Joshawa stuck to the letter of that greemint too. He sure give them Gibby-uns the more meenyell of the jobs, and them people has bin hewers and drores of water ever since.

CHAPTER 10

The rest of them tribes was not like yer Gibby-uns. They gang up to smite them fer been in leeg with Joshawa.

6 Them Gibby-uns run to Joshawa, and sed, "You gotta help us like it sez heer in the fine print of this contrack."

11 Joshawa was as good as His wurd, and God kep His wurds too, and throo down grate stones of hale frum Hevvin which dun even more dammidge than the sords of Izzreal.

12 Joshawa need more time fer his cleenup of his ennemys, and tole the Sun fer to stand still and the Moon to wate, wile he finish the job.

13 Everybuddy laff, but by God it happen. Joshawa got mebby a fortyate hour day outa it. Them was Joshawa's finest hours.

THE BOOK OF JEDGES

CHAPTER 1

Joshawa hung on till a hunnert and ten, then went to his mountin jist like Moeziz had dun. But before he went he put a big stone under an oaktree fer to remind his peeple that God wud still be hevvy upon them if they fergot He wuz there.

2 And all them Izzrealites thot, whose gonna look after us now?

CHAPTER 4

It wernt long before they was all doon evil agin, rite in site of ther Lord.

2 Along cum a Cane-in king who was more modren than the rest.

3 He had nine hunnert charryits bilt of arn. He dint waste much time rollin over them childern of Izzreal.

4 Took a woman to git them outa trubble this time. She wuz Debra, a lady judge and profitess.

5 Cooden have much of a livin, fer she livved under a pam tree. But she musta bin good at the judgin, fer all kindsa peeple cum to her fer advice.

6 Incloodin, Barrack, the lokel hed-man whom God had commanded to riz up and fite yer Caninites.

7 Debra jist told Barrack to do what God had tole him to do.

8 But Barrack confided to her, "I'll go if yule cum along. Otherwise, no dice."

9 Debra had herd that God wud sell ther enemmy into the hands of a woman, so she figgered it was her. She cum along.

10 So Barrack went up with ten thou men and this one woman aginst nine hundert arn charryits.

14 Debra sed fer to do it, on accounta the Lord wud take care of all them big wheels, arn and all.

15 It cum to pass. Them vehickles was beat by God.

Debra stumps fer God

17 Sizzerer, the ennemy leeder got offa his charryit and run. He run strait to Jail, witch wuz the name of the wife of one of them Canin-ites.

18 He snuck in her tent and ast fer a drink.

19 He wanted water, she give him milk, and cuvverd him with a mantel.

20 He tole her to tell whoever cum by, there was no man here.

21 Jail took a nail and hammer and made shure she wazn't tellin no fib, by smoatin him hard by the Temples, and tackin him rite into the ground, while he was takin a nap. It becum permamint.

22 When they ast her if she had a live one with her, she tole them no lies.

24 Izzrealites won. Cane-in, nuthing.

CHAPTER 6

Wernt long before God's children of Izzreal was kickin over the traces agin. God jist throo up His hands, and deelivert them to the Middlnites. It wuz a seven-yeer deel.

5 Wen them Middlnites move in, them Izzrealites hadda move out, up into yer hills and caves and other substanderd housing.

6 Whatever Izzreal had soan, them Middlnites et up.

7 There wuz more of them than grasshoppers. And they brung along camels too. That tuk care of the water supply.

8 They all cryed out, O Lord send us a profit to make up fer this loss.

11 God sent down one of his Angels, who sat under a oaktree watchin a yung fella called Giddy'un thrashing his wheat beside a still. He was in the bizness of makin hay by sunshine and makin wine by moonshine fer to hide it frum the Middlnites.

12 This Angel watch Giddy'un fer a wile, then all of a suddint spoke up. "What's with you, Giddyun?" Giddyun jist froze. "I'll tell you what, Giddy'un, the Lord is with you."

13 Giddy'un sed back, "If that's the case then why did we git all packed up frum Ejippt jist to be deelivert to them Middlnites.

14 God tuk over from that Angel and spoke dreckly to Giddy'un. "I'm gonna pass a meerackle. Yer it."

15 Giddy'un gulp and sed, "Oh Lord, you pickt the runt of the litter".

16 God sed, "Yew and I are gonna smight them Middlnites, as one man, and yer him."

17 Giddy'un gulp again and ast, "D'you have any identify-a-cayshun, Lord just so's Ile know it's Yew.

18 Jist a minit, and I'll git you a little present, in case it's Yew."

19 Giddy'un cum back with a kid, and unlevvied cakes and some flower, and whipt it all up into a meal.

20 God sed, "Put them cakes and that kid on this here rock."

12 It got dun, and God touch them with the end of his staff, and the hole thing went up in smoke.

22 Giddy'un thot the meel was roont but he shure knew Who he'd bin talkin to.

23 Somewheres he herd God say

"Don't be scairt, yew won't die."

24 Giddy'un, he bilt a alter.

25 God tole him to knock off the alter to Bail that Giddy'un's father had bilt.

27 He dun this by nite, so's his old man wooden know.

28 Nex mornin everybuddy was wundrin who had cast-off Bail and put up this new alter.

30 When they found it wuz Giddy'un, they tole his dad Joe Ash to bring out his boy fer to be the first sackerfice on it.

31 But Giddy'un's dad sed, "Let my boy go fer Bail? Whose god are you fer annyways? Let Bail look out fer hisself. Anybuddy bow-in down to him round these parts is lookin fer trubble."

33 But them Middlnites and them Mallykites, crost the river and campt it up together in the same valley as the Izzrealites.

34 Giddy'un he bloo his trumpit. Nobuddy knew what had got into him, but sum sed it was the Spearit of the Lord. He was callin on all his tribe fer to folly him.

36 Then Giddy'un sed to God, "It's not that I don't trust Ye, but You sed You'd deliver us all by Hand, and jist to make shure, I'm layin this sheep's flees on the floor overnite.

37 Cum mornin if there's dew on the flees and none on the ground, I'll bleeve it."

38 Nex mornin Giddy'un was squeezin out the flees and them drops was fallin on arrid ground.

39 So Giddy'un sed to God, "Please don't think I'm septickal, but lemme try that one more time, only the other ways round."

40 God dun it. Nex mornin the flees was dry and there was dew on the ground.

CHAPTER 7

That dun it fer Giddy'un. He took all his bunch and camp across the river frum them Middlnites. His trumpit had brung in mebby thirty-two thou men.

2 But God sed, "Too menny men. Peeple will say that they was the ones wun over them Middlnites, and this is gonna be My battle.

3 Send home them as don't feel like stayin, on accounta been scairt." Giddy'un gulp, but he spoke what the Lord sed, and twenty-two thou up and beat it.

4 God sed, "Ten thou is still too menny. Give em all a drink down by the riverside."

5 Giddy'un brung them all to the edge and tole them to help therselfs. But God sed, "Mind how they drink. Them as neel down and cups with ther hands is out, and them as laps like dogs is in."

6 Giddy'un near had a fit. There was only three-hunnert dog-lappers.

7 God sed, "That's all we need fer to dee-liver them Middlnites. Tell the rest to go on home."

9 That nite God sed, "Go and check out yer Middlnite camp.

10 If yer scairt take sum buddy with you.

11 But overhear what them Middlnites are tockin about." Giddy-un took his hired man Poor-Uh with him.

12 Them Middlnites and Mally-kites was thickern lowcussts, not to menshun ther camels.

13 But Giddy'un overherd one Middlnite tellin a dreem to a fella Middy at one of their campfires. "I dreamt I seen this cake fall into our camp, hit one of our tense, knocker upside down and layer flat."

14 His comrad sed, "That upside-down cake is Giddy'un and that's jist what he's gonna do to us."

15 Giddy'un felt releef, worshipped God, and cum home to camp. He tole his troops ther was nuthin to worry about.

16 He divvy up all his men into three cumpnys, and give them all trumpits and empty jars with candels inside. Everybuddy look at Giddy'un sidewaze and thot: "What are we sposed to do with this here?"

17 Giddy-un sed, "Jist do what I do. When we cum up to them Middlnite outskirts, and I blow, you blow too. And don't fergit to shout our teem yell, 'Fur the Lord and Giddy'un!!' "

19 Giddy'un took a hunnert of the men with him, and tole them not to fergit ther jars. Them Middlnites was jist windin up ther middle watch, when Giddy'un and his boys snuck up on them. Jist as they was settin' ther watches, the Giddy'uns bloo ther trumpits and smashed ther jars.

20 Them other two cumpnees dun the same with ther jars and trumpits, jist smash and bloo. Everybuddy yelt: "A sord fer the Lord and fer Giddy'un!"

21 You woodena bleeved what happen. Them three hunnert made sich a ringtale snorter of a din, that all them Middys and Malaykys jump up and fleed, every witchwaze.

Sum of them fleed into ther own peeples sords. You never seen such a mix-up.

22 Now Giddy'un sent fer all them other Izrealite tribes fer to help him chase Middlnites.

CHAPTER 8

Sum of them Izzrealites, naimly yer tribe of Eefrin', wuzn't too please about bein leff outa the first part of the battle.

2 But Giddy'un sed, "What I dun was nuthin ... I jist sode the seed. Now you fellers kin harvest yer gripes of rath." They fergive him and started hootin after yer Middlnites.

3 This kinda thing gives man a appytite.

4 Giddy'un's boys was faint frum hunger.

5 They stopped by Sook Oth and ast fer bred.

6 But the Sook Others sed, "When you've won you'll git bred, not till then. Cum back and form a bredline later."

7 Giddy'un sed, "When I cum back Ile flail you with a bryer, that's what I'll do."

8 He went on to Pen-you-ill and they give him the same answer.

9 He sed, "When I cum again in peece, it'll be yer town tower that'll be in peeces."

13 Giddy-un knock off them Middlnites, cum back with two of ther kings.

14 He cum back by way of Sook Oth, showed them his pair of Kings, and beat them all with ther own bryer bushes.

17 He past by Pen-you-ill, and compleetly broke up ther lokel hi-rize Tower.

22 The men of Izzreal was delited with Giddy'un and ast him to be ther rooler, and his son and his grandson and so on after him.

23 But Giddy'un sed, "None of us is gonna rool over you, that's the Lord's job.

24 All I want is you men to give me yer eerings." (A lotta them Ishy-Male-Ites wore sich things, back then.)

25 Everybuddy pitch in ther eerings to the toon of seventeen hunnert sheckles worth. Not countin yer cressents and pendents and purpel robes got offa them Middylnite Kings, and the collers offa them camel necks.

28 Fer the time bean, Izzreal was safe and them Middlnites was sub-dude and hung down ther heds for the next forty yeer.

32 Giddy'un died of a good ole age, and left behind 70 sons, incloodin one by his conkyoubine, who seems to be naimless but the issyuh of her loins is call A-bim-a-lick.

CHAPTER 9

A-bim-a-lick as soon as he got old enuff, started stumpin around fer to be King.

2 He ast all his peeple wether they'd druther be rooled over by him or by them other 70 sons of Giddy'un.

3 Natcherly, bein plite, they all sed "Oh we'd love to be rooled by yew, A-bim-a-lick." They all give him a peece of silver and hoped he'd mebby git drunk and fergit about it.

4 But A-bim-a-lick went strait home and kilt all his bruthers, sept one, Jot-him. Still, 69 outa 70 is sum score.

5 Jot-him hid when A-bim-a-lick becum King.

7 But wernt long before Jot-him got up on a mountin top and sound off agin his bruther.

8 He tole everybuddy a story. More like a parble, reely. Here it is. "The trees wuz lookin fer a King. They ast the olive tree to rain over them.

9 But the oliv sed, 'Yew think I'd leave my oily depossits jist to be per-moted over all yew trees?'

10 So the trees went over to yer fig and ast it to be boss.

11 But the fig sed, 'What? Give up my sweetness and all my liddle froots, fer to take on all that?'

12 So they ast the vine to be over them.

13 The vine sed, 'You think I'm gonna leeve my wine? Yer crazy.'

14 They finely got down to the brambull.

15 Brambull sed, 'If I take the job, then yer gonna be in my shadow. Do you trust me? If you don't I'll git so burnt up there won't be a seeder left in Lebnon.'

19 What's the morale of this story? Jot-him sed, "If you reely trooly sin-seerly want A-bim-a-lick fer King, insted of my father Giddy'un that-was, or enny one of my 69 bruthers he kilt, that's fine.

20 If not, fire is gonna cum outa A-bim-a-lick and yer the ones is gonna be burned up."

21 After this Jot-him run to Beer

and staid there, fer feer of bruther A-bim-a-lick, now King.

22 Nuthin much happent in the first three years of his rain.

23 But God got back at him fer dooin whut he dun to his 69 brethren.

24 He sent a evil spearit down.

52 Finely A-bim-a-lick got his while beseeching a tower. Sum woman drop a milled stone on his hed fer to brake his skull.

54 It did.

CHAPTER 11

Jepthaw was a Gilly-Ad-ite, and the sunuva harlit.

2 His family kick him out on accounta he was borne by a wrong woman.

4 But when the Amma-nites started warrin agin Gilly-Ad, they all ast him to cum back.

7 Jepthaw sed, "How cum yew want me now when I wuzn't goodenuff before?"

8 They sed, "Never mine. Jist be our hed."

12 So Jepthaw becum hed captin, and sent a messidge to them Amma-nites saying, "What's the trubble?"

13 And King Amm sed, "Yer bunch took away my land when you cum up frum Ejippt. I want it back, is all."

24 Jepthaw sed, "We never druv you out. Our God did. We jist repossesst becuz He tole us to."

30 Jepthaw also checked with God and sed, "Git us outa this, and I'll give You anything. Incloodin what's in my house, and whatever cums out the door first when I cum home.

That'll be a garnteed bernt offrin."

32 So Jepthaw fot them Amma-nites and God delivered.

34 Mebby Jepthaw figgered his missus wud cum out to meet him, but no. Out cum his dotter and ownly child.

35 She was dancin and singin to beat the band, but Jepthaw he jist tore his close and wisht he'd never opened his mouth.

36 But the dotter sed, "A bargin is a bargin.

37 Jist let me go way to the mountings with sum frends fer a cuppla munths and bewhale my virjinnity."

38 He sed go and she went.

39 She cum back, brown as a berry having not known no man, and ended up as a bernt offrin.

40 She's bin morned ever sints four days a yeer.

CHAPTER 13

The childern of Izzreal started cuttin up agin, so God delivert them over to yer Fillasteins fer the next forty yeer.

2 A lot of wimmen were barn. No chants of childern.

3 God spoke to one and sed, "Yule bare a son." The woman cooden conseeve of sich a thing.

4 God sed, "Lay off drinkin and rottin food.

5 And when you raze yer son, don't never cut his hair, and I garntee he'll deliver all of yous out of Fillastein hands."

6 She tole her huzbin.

8 He wanted to see fer hisself.

9 So God cum agin and when He did, the woman run and got her huzbin.

Jepthaw's dotter bewhaling her virjinnity to her friends

19 He was so overcum, he run quick to git a kid to sackerfice on a rock.

20 When the flame went up you cud see the Angel of the Lord in it and the cupple fell flat on ther faces.

22 He sed to his wife, "We'll shurely die now we've seen His face."

23 But the woman had more sense, and figgerd the Lord was shoan them all this fer a speshul reesin.

24 The reezin was ther baby. He was speshul. Call him Samsin.

CHAPTER 14

Samsin grew up fast.

2 Wernt long before he wuz a-cortin. Speshully them Fillastein girls.

4 But his pairnts knew God wooden like that.

5 He went down to look the Fillastein girls over, and cum across a lion.

6 Samsin was cot bare-handed, but he tore that lion apart like it was a kid. (FOOTNOTE: But he never toll his pairnts about this.)

7 He took a fansty to one girl and sed he'd be back to taker.

8 On his wayback, he cum acrosst that ded lion's carkass, witch was now the home fer a bees hive.

9 This give Samsin a idee fer a riddel to tell at the ingagemint party he was givin fer the Fillastein girl.

12 He offert to give a prize fer the guesser of this riddel ... thirty sheets and thirty changes of close.

13 "But if ya cant guess, then that's exackly what you owe me."

14 Here was the riddel: "Out of the eeter cum sumthin to eat, Outa the strong, cum sumthin sweet."

15 After seven days the guests was about to give up. The weddin went ahed thru all this, so they figgert Samsin's new wife shood know the anser. By this time they was so fed up tryna guess that they sed to her, "Git the anser outa yer huzbin or we'll bern down yer house with you in it, becuz we cant afford all them sheets and cloze changes jist fer yer weddin presents."

16 Samsin's wife cum to him weepin. "You tole a riddel," she snift, "and you never even tole me the anser." He sed, "I never tole my own pairnts, why shood I tell you?"

17 She musta wept fer seven days, near drove him up the wall, so he finely tole her, and natcherly she tole them Fillastein gests.

18 So they tole Samsin the anser: "What's sweetern hunny, And Strongern a lion?" Samsin look them all strait in the face and sed, "Yooda never got my riddel if you hadna plowed with my heffer."

19 Samsin musta bin mad, becuz he sloo thirty of them, and went back home.

20 So his bride was give to the best man.

CHAPTER 15

Awhile after, roundybout harvist time, Samsin cum back fer a visit, and he brung along a kid fer his wife. But her father sed, "She's bizzy in the bed chaimber.

2 We thot you'd leff her behind, so we give her to yer best man. How bout her young sister?"

4 Samsin was so mad he went out

Samsin — 1 Lyin — 0

and cot three hundert foxes, tied them tale to tale, and put a torch tween ther tales.

5 He let them firey foxes go in the Fillasteins standin korn, rite next to ther vinyards and olives.

6 The Fillasteins was as shocked and burnt up as much as ther korn. The Fillasteins figgerd the thing to do was to bern Samsin's wife and fatherinlaw.

7 Samsin sed, "Ile get even jist this wunts, then I'll stop."

8 He smote them hip and thigh. There wuz a grate slotter. After that he went and end up in the clef of a rock.

9 The Fillasteins cum after him, fer to put him in a bind.

10 This was in Joodah, and the Izzrealites who lived there was nerviss about Samsin. "Don't you know them Fillasteins is our boss? What are you tryna do?"

11 Sez Samsin, "Jist what they dun to me."

12 But the Joodyites sed, "We've cum to deliver you to the Fillasteins in a packidge deal." So they bind him up in a set of new cords.

14 But when they brung him to Fillastein country, God cum down and terned them cords to flacks, and bernt them up with fire, loosing his hands.

15 Samsin grab the jawbone outa sum ass, and dun it to about a thousand Fillasteins, beeting the ass's jawbone offa alla them.

18 That was thirsty work, and Samsin was afrayed he'd die parcht and fall into the hands of them as was uncircle-sized.

19 But God clave out a holler place in that assjaw, unlock it, and water cum out.

20 Them Izzreelites was open-jawd and made Sam's Son a jedge fer the next twenny yeers.

CHAPTER 16

Samsin went down to Gazza and got mix up with a harlit.

2 This is not thot to be good fer jedges. The lokel peeple thot they'd lay-in-wate and cum mornin, kill him.

3 But Samsin got up about midnite, took the dores offa the sitty gaits, and the posts too, put 'em on his shoulders, bars and all, and walk off with them all up to the topova hill. Nobuddy follered.

4 After that he went down in a valley and fell in with a woman call Dee Lyler.

5 The Fillasteins got after her fer to find out what made him so strong. They offert her elevenhundert peeces of silver. She took it.

6 Dee sed, "Wherd you git them mussels, big boy? And what makes you weak, besides me?"

7 Samsin sed, "Tie me up with seven wet boastrings and I'm jist as weak as the nexman."

8 The Fillasteins got the stuff and Dee Lyler tied him up.

9 The Fillasteins was under the bed, and Dee Lyler tole him that. He jist snap them strings like they was straw, and sed, "Ha, ha!" You never seen sich scurryin Fillasteins.

10 Dee Lyler was putout. "You foolt me, Samsin. What reely makes you knuckle under?"

11 He sed, "Try new-moan ropes never bin used."

Short, back and sides?

12 She dun it that way, and tole him about the liars-in-wate. He jist laft and brake them binders frum offa his arms like thred.

13 Dee sed, "You fool me agin. Cum on. Stop lyin."

14 Samsin sed, "Do up my harelocks with a pin and I'm jist a hand fulla putty." She dun him up in tite pincurls and called in the Fillasteins. But he woke up, pulled out the pin, and bang, there was wild hare, and wilder Fillasteins all over the place.

15 Dee Lyler sed, "Samsin yer not with me. How kin you say you luv me when you do me like you do?"

16 She kept after him, till he got fed up with her nag, nag, nag.

17 He finely tole her, "I've never had a haircut sints I was born. God tole my muther to leeve it lay. That's what makes me speshul."

18 Dee Lyler sed to the Fillasteins, "Cum and bring yer sheckles." They cum and crost her pam with silver.

19 She tole Samsin to sleep on her knees, and she callt in a barber when her man was asleep, and he shave alla the lox offa Samsin's hed. Shure enuff, he went all limp.

20 She tole him, "Here cum them Fillasteins." Samsin figgerd it was time fer to shake hisself, but ther was nuthin much shakin' with Samsin now.

21 The Fillasteins cum, Samsin was put out, and so wuz his eyes. He end up workin in the prizun gristmill.

22 But that hair started groan agin.

23 The Fillasteins went off to have a party fer ther god, Day-gone, fer de-activatin Samsin.

25 They all got a bit merry, and thot they shood bring Samsin to the party fer to make fun of him.

26 Samsin was led on to this party, and stuckup tween two pillers so's they cud throw things at him.

27 Everybuddy was at the party. About three thou mennen women. It was a big do, and Samsin was the ennertanemint.

28 He ast God fer his strenth back, jist this one more time.

29 Everybuddy was laffin at him, as he leened aginst them two pillers. Then he bowed to alla them Fillasteins and brot down the house.

30 Ther was no encores. It was curtins fer everybuddy.

THE
BOOK OF ROOF

CHAPTER 1

Izzreal went back to Jedges after trying jist one King. But it dint alwaze help. Jedges cant stop famins.

2 Sum peeple immigratered to Moe-Ab. Even inter-married up.

3 One Izzreal woman Nayomey got widderd over there, so she thot

she shood cum back home to Joodah.

6 Her two dotters-in-law, Roof and Orrpah, was widderd too. They was both Moe Abitesses.

8 So Nayomey sed, "You two girls better skeeter on back to yer mothers."

9 But these two Moebite girls liked ther mother-in-law, and wanted to cum with her.

12 "You won't git no more huzbins frum me, girls. Even if I cud bare froot, you wooden wanna hang around til my lil fellas wuz full groan." She kid them a bit.

13 Orrpah laff and kiss her mother-in-lore goobye. But Roof hung around and clung.

15 Nayomey sed, "What are you hangin round fer? Git along with yer sistern-law."

16 But Roof jist sed, "Where you go, I go. Yer folks shall be mine. And that goes fer Gods too."

22 So Nayomey cum home back to Izzreal. She sed she left full and cum back empty, but there was Roof rite behinder.

CHAPTER 2

Back heer in Joodah it was barly harvist. Nayomey had rich kinfoke so she hedded fer them, and Roof drug along after. Nayomey's cuzzin Bo-As wuz reapin his feelds. Roof sed, "Do you think yer cuzzin wud mind if I gleened up after him?"

3 Nayomey sed "Go, girl, go." Roof went, and Bo-ass notissed her amung the sheefs. "Whose girl is she?"

4 He give orders to let her glean up all his feelds, and give her a drink.

10 Roof fell on her face after that, on accounta she was a immigrunt.

11 But Bo-As sed, "Enny girl who is nice to her mothern-lore enuff to folley her a long ways frum home, is my kind of girl."

CHAPTER 3

Nayomey was anckshuss fer to marry Roof off agin.

2 She herd Bo-As wuz thrashing all nite on the barn flore.

3 She tole Roof to take a bath, and git down to that flore. "But don't give yerself away till he's ate and drunk.

4 And when he turns in, you mark the spot, git there, and uncover his feet, and he'll be tickle pink with you."

5 Roof dun everythin her motherin-lore tole her.

7 Bo-As was feelin no pain, lyin down on sum corn husks, when Roof cum along, when he was sounder sleep. She uncover his feets and laid down alongside him.

8 Long bout midnite, he open a eye, seen this strange woman lyin there and sed, "Whodat?"

9 She sed, "I'm yer hand-made Roof. Spred yer skert over me, and we kin make arrangemints, since yer awreddy my kinsfoke by marriage."

10 Bo-As sed, "I thot you'd be wantin mebby one of them yunger fellas!

12 There is a neerer Kinsman than me. He has a pryer clame. You kin try him in the mornin.

13 If he don't want yuh fer kin, I do. Meenwile stay here and lay at my feet."

14 Roof dun this, but got up erly

Roof tooken to the gleaners

so's noone wud notiss. Even Bo-As sed, "Nobuddy menshun there was a woman in here last nite!" (FOOTNOTE: Even tho they both dun nothin to be ashame about.)

15 Before she went, Bo-As ast her to take the vale she wore and hold it outstretch. Then he laid on her six mezzyours of barly, fer her mothern-law.

CHAPTER 4

Bo-As want to check out that neerer kinsman. He went strait to the gate and wate till he cum along. He finely did, and Bo-As ast him to take a lode offa his feet.

2 Bo-As tole him that Nayomey had a passle of land fer to sell belonging to her huzbin-that-was.

3 "Do you want it er not?" sed Bo-As.

4 "I want it," sed this kinsman.

5 "Ther's a girl, Roof, goes along with it," Bo-As tole him.

6 "I got nuff complickayshuns thout that," sed the kinsman and he tole Bo-As to buy it hisself. And he tuck off his shoe and give it to Bo-As which wuz the weerd custum in them parts.

7 But that made it a deal, and Bo-As bot the ole homested, and Roof cum along with it.

8 Nobuddy minded he wuz marryin a Moe-bite-ess. They all shivareed them and wisht all ther trubbles wuz little ones.

13 Not too long after Roof had a baybee boy.

14 Everybuddy expeckted grate things of this little un.

17 And they was rite. Fer he becum the grandfather of King Dave Id, soon to cum.

THE
FIRST BOOK OF SAM YELL

CHAPTER 1

Hanner was loved by the Lord, but He had shut up her woom.

6 She was married to a man had two wives. The other woman, Paneena teezed her about it till she wuz sore.

7 Yeer after yeer she'd cum up empty-handed.

8 Her huzbin dint mind. He sed he'd druther have her than ten sons. (Sides, he had a spair takin care of that sorta thing anyhow.)

9 Hanner finely went to the preest about it.

10 She was bittern ever and had wept till she was sore, allover agin.

11 She vowed to God if she got frootfull she wud give it back to the Lord and see to it her child never got a haircut.

12 The preest marked her mouth when she sed that.

13 Her lips was moovin but nuthin was comin out. The preest jist thot Hanner was drunk.

14 So he sed to her, "Git offa that stuff."

15 But Hanner sed she wernt drunk, jist porin out her heart to the Lord.

20 It dun sum gud. She got one. She name him Sam Yell becuz that's what she dun to the Lord to git him.

24 After weenin him, she tuck him up to the Shylow Tempel and loned him to God, jist as she had promist.

CHAPTER 2

Every yeer when she brung up her yeerly sackerfice with her huzbin, she seen Sam Yell and brung him a lil coat.

21 God give her three sons and two dotters after that to make up fer the lone.

CHAPTER 3

Sam Yell becum like a son to the Hypreest Eeleye. Which was gud, becuz his own two sons was regler hellyuns.

2 Eeleye's eyes begun to wax all over and becum dim.

3 One nite, young Sam Yell was asleep hard by the Ark in the tempel.

4 He herd sumwun call his name, and figgerd it was ole Eeleye.

5 He run to him, and sed, "Here I am." But Eeleye sed, "Go back to bed, yer heerin things."

6 Sam Yell was called up agin. Back to Eeleye, and back agin to bed.

8 He got call back the third time, and bother old Eeleye agin. Eeleye finely figgerd it was a call frum On High.

9 Eeleye tole Sam Yell to go back to bed agin, and wate fer the call frum Up There.

10 Shure enuff, the Lord cum and stud at the foot of his bed, and when he called Sam Yell's name he wuz all ears.

11 And God tole Sam Yell He was gonna do sumthin in Izzreal wud make everybuddy's eers sit up and tingel.

13 It was on accounta Eeleye's rottin sons, who had never bin traned or restraned by Eeleye.

17 Next mornin ole Eeleye ast Sam Yell what God had sed.

18 Sam Yell tole him everything, spairin none of the deetales. Eeleye he shrug, and sed, "Let God do what seems good, be all rite with me."

19 Sam Yell grew up and God overherd everythin he sed.

20 By that time everybuddy knew he was cut out to be a jenna-wine profit.

CHAPTER 4

Them Fillasteins was at it agin.

2 Beetin the Izzrealites.

3 They got beet so bad, them Izzrealers figgered the only weppin they had left was ther holey of holeys, the Ark of the Covernant.

4 Them two no-gud sonsa Eeleye, Hop-nee and Finny-hass was the ones brung it out of Shylow and into the feeld of war.

6 Wen the Fillasteins herd what the shouten was about they got the wind up.

7 They was afrayed of that Ark. They knew God was inside it, and they membered He was the one brung all them plaigs upon the Ejippshuns.

9 They figgerd if they lost this battel, they mite be Hebroo slaves fer the rest of ther Fillastein lives.

10 So they fot hard, and it was the Izzreals end up smitten. Thirty thou of them, incloodin' Hop-knee and Finny-hass.

11 The Ark was took too.

12 The fella that brung the news to Eeleye, had his close rent rite out, and heeps of dirt on his hed.

14 Everybuddy in town was cryin about that Ark. When Eeleye herd the catter-wallin he ast what all the noise was about.

15 By now ole Eeleye was ninety-ate, almost as dim as his eyes.

16 The massinger tole him about the battel, and about his two sons gettin it in the neck.

17 Eeleye lissen to all that, not moovin, but when he was tole about the Ark been stole, he fell backerds offa his seet, brake his neck and end up ded.

CHAPTER 5

The Fillasteins took that Ark over to ther place, and set it up hard by ther own god, Day-Gonn.

3 Next mornin, Day-Gonn was lyin on his face flat in the erth. They set him up agin.

4 Next day he was flat on his face agin, oney permamint, becuz his hed wuz off, and the pams of his hands too. Nobuddy thot to stump him up agin.

5 That was oney the start.

6 God smote them Fillasteins with emmer-rods and He was hevvy handed with them. (FOOTNOTE: Emmer Rods is Boyls.)

7 Them Fillasteins figgerd they better git rid of that Ark.

8 Sumbuddy took it to Gath.

9 The Gathers wernt happy about that, fer God smote them with emmer-rods even in ther secret parts.

10 They tryed the same thing in Akron, but the Akronites sed, "Git that Thing outa here before it slays us."

CHAPTER 6

Them Fillasteins sent that Ark back in a hurry, and presents along with it too. Five gold boyls in mammary of what God had sent upon them, and five gold rats in onner of the plaig they mite of had.

7 They hitch the hole thing up to a cart with two cows in front, without a yoke betweenem.

8 The Fillasteins let them cows loose on the hyway fer to see if that Ark cud find its way home without no driver.

13 Them cattel hedded strait fer Izzrealite parts, and cum upon sum farmers reeping in ther valley.

14 They all whoop when they seen the Ark and a cupple of them looked inside fer to check it out.

19 That was the last look-in they ever dun. God smote them fer that, and He musta bin fulla rath, becuz 50,080 got smitted also.

CHAPTER 7

The Ark end up in the house of Abinadab. Everybuddy else seem ascairt to take it on.

2 It staid there twenty yeer.

3 Sam Yell tole everybuddy that the Lord was back with them, and

He was the oney one cud deliver, and to put down all them forn tinhorn gods.

4 The Izzrealites were still frayed of the Fillasteins and ast Sam Yell to perteck them.

9 But Sam Yell sed oney God cud do that, and offert up a bernt lamb.

10 The Fillasteins smelt the lamb and cum near, but grate thunderin cum down frum God and put them Fillasteins in discomfert.

11 They was then chaste after by Izzrealites, and smoted, and never cum back as long as Sam Yell was around.

16 Sam Yell kept on the jedgin circus from town to town till he got too old and let his sons do the jedgin.

CHAPTER 8

S am Yell's boys was not chips offa the old jedgemint block.

3 They took munny under the table, fer one thing and anuther.

4 Everybuddy knew it too. They tole Sam Yell his sons was preeverted jedges.

5 They sed, "We're sick of jedges ennyway. Git us a king like other fokes has."

6 Sam Yell dint know what to say. So he prayed.

7 The Lord sed, "These peeple arnt reejectin you. They're treetin Me like a reejeck. They want a King so's I won't rain over them.

8 They bin doin this to Me since I brung them out Ejippt and they're doin it agin.

9 Do what they ast, but remine them what rong they're doin at the same time."

10 Sam Yell relayd all this back to the peeple.

11 "If you git a King, he'll keep you on the run in fronta his charryit," Sam Yell tole them.

12 "You'll do all his work fer him, and he'll never mind yores.

13 He'll take yer dotters and make them bake cakes.

14 He'll take the best of yer feelds and give them to his servints.

15 Ten purrsent of yer seed goes to him.

16 Yer asses will work fer him.

17 And one tense of yer sheep. Not to mention yew all.

18 You'll be belly-akin' about this fore long, and the Lord won't heer you."

19 Nobuddy lissened. They wanted a king to be in stile like everybuddy elts.

20 They figgered a king wud fite ther battels fer them.

22 God sed to Sam Yell "Give them a king. Serves them rite."

CHAPTER 9

B en Kish had a son name Sol, hy and mitey frum his sholders upward.

21 They was both Benjy Mites, the smallest tribe of the bunch.

22 But Sam Yell sent fer Sol, and took him into the parler and sit him in the best chair.

CHAPTER 10

S am Yell pored oil over Sol's hed and kist him and that was it.

9 As Sol turn his back on Sam Yell, God give young Sol anuther

heart, fit fer a King. But he wuzn't a profit, like Sam Yell.

10 On his way home, Sol cum acrost a bunch jibberin and jabberin and profitsyin all over the place.

11 Sol started doin all this too, till peeple sed, "Is our Sol gonna be a profit or a King?"

14 When he cum home his unkle ast him, "Where you bin, and what you bin doin?"

16 Sol never tole him a thing.

21 Sam Yell dun it for him. He tole the hole land Kish's boy Sol was Kingpin.

22 Nobuddy cud find Sol then. But God cud. He tole where Sol was hiding. Mungst the baggidge!

23 They brung Sol out and lift him over ther heds, makin him above everybuddy rite frum the start.

24 They all shout, "God save the King."

27 Sept fer the children of Bell Ile, who sed: "How is he gonna save us?" And they brung him no presents. But Sol held his peece. He knew he had presents of his own. He was hyer'n enny of his peeple frum his sholders upward.

CHAPTER 13

When Sol had bin raining fer two yeer he got into a fite with the Fillasteins.

2 They cum together at Mickmash, which is exackly what happen.

3 Sol's boy Johnnythum dun good.

5 But the Fillasteins had thirty thou charryits and six thou cavillry.

6 When the Izzrealites seen all

that, they hid anywares they cud: caves, thickits, up on rocks, under rocks, and even in the pits.

8 Old Sam Yell he staid away frum all this.

9 But Sol ast him to cum quick and make a bernt offrin.

10 Sam Yell wernt that quick enny more, so Sol did one up hisself.

11 Sam Yell cum a bit later, snift the air, and sed, "What have you dun, Sol?" Sol sed, "The Fillasteins was here in sich force, I hadda force myself to make the offrin."

13 Sam Yell pull a long face and tole Sol he was foolish, and dun sumthin he wuzn't sposed to.

14 "That dun it," sed Sam Yell. "Now God's gonna find sumbuddy elts. A man after his own heart."

CHAPTER 14

Johnnythum wuzn't scairt of them Fillasteins. He snuck off without tellin his dad, Sol.

6 Him and the young fella that help him bare arms went rite up to yer Fillastein garson.

12 The Fillasteins took one look at them two and sed, "Cum on up to us, and we'll show you a thing er two."

14 Johnnythum knew the Lord was on his side, and he knockoff twenny of them Fillasteins. It was a garson finish.

23 The Lord shure save that day.

24 Sol he thot he cud win by stickin to the rools. He tole his peeple not to eat nuthin till nite cum.

27 Johnnythum didden know nuthin about this. He took sum hunny on the run.

28 He got back to camp with a sticky mouth, and everybuddy sed, "Yer gonna catch it frum the Ole Man. We cant eat till dark even tho everybuddy's reddy to faint."

29 Johnnythum sed, "My dad's nuts. That hunny kept me goin.

30 If yood all hadda good square meal, you mite-a beaten all of them Fillasteins."

32 Everybuddy was so starvin, they all grab the neerst sheep er ox, er caff, and practickly et it raw, bludden all.

33 Sol was fit to bust when he herd. He wuz reddy to roll a grate stone on alla them.

39 He was so mad at his boy Johnnythum he put him up fer death. Nobuddy sed a murmur, but they thot a lot.

40 But Sol cud tell they was thinkin sumthin. So he sed:

42 "Cast a lot tween me and my boy. Which one is rite?"

45 All the peeple sed: "Yer gonna kill yer boy who save us all today? God ferbid!"

CHAPTER 15

God did too. Old Sam Yell never seen Sol no more till he got ded.

CHAPTER 16

But that wernt jist yet. In the meantime God sed to Sam Yell, "Stop moonin bout Sol, fill yer horn with oil, and go out and git me anuther King."

2 Sam Yell sez: "If Sol heers I'm out doin that, he'll kill me."

3 God sed, "Take a heffer with you over to Jessie's place and pertend yer makin a sackerfice."

4 Jessie, he live over to Beth-lee-hem. When the old fellas in that town seen Sam Yell heddin ther way, they all got nerviss, at what mite be up.

5 Sam Yell sed, "Relacks. I'm here to sankteefy all of you, speshully Jessie and sons."

10 Jessie had eight sons. Seven pass before Sam Yell, who sed:

11 "Got enny more?" Jessie sed his youngest was out in the sheepish pastyours.

12 He was brung in. Good looking boy, name of Dave Id. God sed, "That's him."

13 Sam Yell empty the horn of oil over his hed, and the spearit of the Lord cum down upon him.

14 At the same time that spearit depart from Sol, and he wuz in trubble from then on.

15 All of Sol's servints thot it was the evil spearits had got him.

16 They thot they'd git him outa hisself with a little mewsick. They avertize fer a good harplayer.

21 That's how Dave Id cum to the court of Sol, and staid on to becum his arm-er-barer.

23 Everytime Dave Id twang that thing, Sol, he felt better.

CHAPTER 17

The Fillasteins was threttnin agin.

4 They had a champ with them, too. Big tall fella frum Gath, Golieth. He was six Cubans tall.

5 He was cuvvered in brass.

7 Hadda a spear that wooden quit.

8 And he stood and cryed in fronta them Izzerealites: "C'mon out an fite!

Yung Dave Id gits ahed

9 Send sumbuddy out to play agin me. If he wins, Ile shine yer shooz, if I win, yule all shine mine."

11 Sol never sed a thing.

12 Jessie's seven sons was up there. They was mum too.

15 Lil Dave Id he was back in his dad's sheepen, feeding flox.

16 Forty days went by, nobuddy tuck up Golieth's offer.

17 Finely, old Jessie back on the homested sed, "My boys must be sicka army grub. Young Dave, take the boys up ten loafs of fresh bred, ten cheezes, and an eefa of parch corn. (FOOTNOTE: An eefa musta bin enuff fer seven hungry full-groan men.)

20 Dave Id riz erly, and left fer the trenches, jist in time to heer Golieth spoutin off agin.

24 He cud hardly hear the big fella fer all them Izzreal knees knockin.

26 Dave Id wondered what they was scairt of. He thot Golieth's knees shood be knockin fer wantin to take on the armys of the livin God.

28 His big bruthers tole Dave Id not to be sich a smart aleck and git back to the sheep.

31 But sumbuddy brung Dave Id's words to Sol, and he was sent fur.

33 Sol sed, "Yer jist a kid, and he's a hevvy-wate champeen."

34 But Dave Id tole him bout the time a lyin and a bear tuck one of his sheep.

35 And he grab that little lamb rite outa the lyin's mouth.

36 And when the lyin cum after him, he grub him by the beerd and sloo him and the bear too.

37 Dave Id sed, "Whoever delivert me frum both paws of the lyin and the bear, will deliver me frum this Fillastein."

38 So Sol got Dave Id up in his armer, and pit a brass helmet on top, and give him a coata male.

39 Dave Id tryed swingin the sword in all that brass, and sed, "I cant go with these." So he shuck them off.

40 He took his sheeper's staff, pickt five liddle rocks outa the streem, and tuck out his trusty slingshot.

41 Golieth seen Dave Id comin on, so he went out to him.

42 But when he seen Dave Id was sitch a litewate he got mad and swore up and down at the boy. "You cum at me with a stick? Whadda ya take me fer? A dog?

44 You take one step neerer, boy, and yule be dogfood."

45 Dave Id stud his ground and sed, "You got all that brass, but I got sumthin better.

46 You cum one step neerer, big boy, and Ile take yer hed off.

47 The Lord has brot you rite inta my hands."

48 Golieth, he rored at all this insulin behaveyer and tuck a jyant step ford.

49 Dave Id jist put his hand in his pockit, tuck a stone and slang it at that Fillastein's fourhed. The stone went rite in, and the big fella plop on his face.

50 Dave Id wunnered what to do next, fer he had no sord.

51 He run to Golieth, grab his outa the sheaf, and hackoff his hed thennen tharewith. When the Fillasteins seen that happen to ther hedman, they all fled.

52 The Izzrealites give a big rore,

and chase them all the way to the gates of Akron.

53 And on the way back they spoiled all ther tense.

57 Dave Id, he went to Sol's tent with Golieth's big hed tuck underneeth his arm.

CHAPTER 18

Dave Id and Sol's boy Johnnythum got along like a house on fire.

4 Johnnythum strip off his robe, garmints, sord, and give it all to Dave Id, rite down to his girdle.

6 When the soldyers cum back to town they was met by all the wimmen dansin.

7 Everybuddy was singin, "Sol he slane thousands, but Dave Id is up in the ten thousands."

8 Sol dint like that.

9 Frum that day, he kep a fishy eye on Dave Id.

10 Perty soon Sol got the evil spearits agin. He sat there with a javalin wile David harp at him.

11 In the middel of a number, Sol throo that javlin hopin to pin Dave Id down a bit. Dave Id hadda duck. Twicet.

CHAPTER 19

Sol tole Johnnythum and all his servints, that Dave Id shood be kilt.

2 Johnnythum tole him that wuz a funny thing to do, after what Dave Id dun.

6 Sol sed he dunno what cum over him. "Jist a mood er a wim, I guess."

7 Johnnythum brung Dave Id back into the hall fer more harping.

9 But Sol got funny agin, and let whoosh with the javaline. Dave Id tuck the hint and excape that nite.

18 Dave Id went strait to ole Sam Yell. And there he staid.

CHAPTER 22

Sol got perty parry-annoyed after this.

8 He felt all his servints was purrspiring aginst him.

CHAPTER 23

The Fillasteins was at it agin, goin aginst the grane by robbin the Izzreal thrashing flores.

2 Dave Id was on speekin terms with the Lord, thanks to Sam Yell, and he ast, "Shall I go agin them Fillasteins?" God sed, "Go, Dave Id, go."

14 Sol still sot Dave Id every day, but God delivert him not.

17 Johnnythum was on Dave Id's side too. He was vote-in fer him as next King of Izzreal, even tho Johnnythum was in line fer the job.

25 Dave Id kep on the moove cuz Sol wuz comin after him.

26 Sol percy-veered but Dave Id wuz alwaze one jump ahed.

CHAPTER 24

Sol had three thou men out helpin him look fer Dave Id, who was on the rocks with the wild gotes.

3 One day, Dave Id was hide-in in a cave, and Sol cum in to cuvver up his feet. Dave Id press aginst the cave side so Sol didden know he wuz there.

4 Dave Id's men sed when Sol snored, "Now's yer chants." Dave Id snuck up with his knife and cut

Sol has it in fer Dave Id

off Sol's skirt frum maxey to minny, jist to show Sol he cud of kilt him, but dint.

5 Afterwards, Dave Id felt tairble about shortening Sol's skirt.

7 When Sol cum outa the cave, Dave Id foller him and apolly-jized.
16 Sol lissen to him, and jist wepped.

17 He tole Dave Id he was more ritejuss than Sol wuz, givin him good fer evil.

20 Sol tole him too, that he was gonna be the reel King of Izzreal but to promise Sol he wooden cut off his seed after him.

21 Dave Id sware, on accounta he wud do nuthin' to his friend Johnnythum.

22 Sol went home. But Dave Id he went back in the cave.

CHAPTER 25
Old Sam Yell finely died.

CHAPTER 26

Dave Id wuz gettin wize. Speshully to Sol and his tanterums. He figgerd Sol wud git him one day. He thot the only way outa Sol's way was to go over to the Fillasteins.

3 He went over to Gath, Golieth's old stompin ground.

4 When Sol lernt Dave Id had dun that, he stopt lookin fer him.

12 He figgerd that by goin over to th'otherside, every Izzrealite wud abhore Dave Id ferever.

CHAPTER 28

Wernt long before the Fillasteins and Izzrealites was at it agin.

The Fillasteins ast Dave Id to fite on their side.

2 They offert to make him hed-keeper of them all.

3 Now that Sam Yell was ded, and Dave Id defecketed to the Fillasteins, Sol dint know who to turn to. He had kickt out all profits, meejums and whizzerds.

5 But when he saw the Fillasteins gatherin, and he knew Dave Id wuz with them, he got scairt.

6 He called on God, but ther was no anser.

7 Sol sed, "Fer hevvin's sake, git me sumbuddy kin get in tutch with the ded." And sumbuddy sed, "I heer tell of an old Indoor witch kin do that."

8 Sol he went in-cogs-neato fer to see her. He ast her to whip up a spearit er two.

9 She tole him that ole King Sol had made all this stuff ill-eagle and she wud be cot ded doin it.

10 Sol sware she wooden be trubbled.

11 So she sez, "Whom shall I bring up from the ded?" And Sol sed, "Sam Yell."

12 The old witch shreek: "Yer Sol!! Why'd you come heer all drest up like Hallyween?"

13 Sol sed, "Cam down. What made you jump like that?" She sed, "I seen Gods dees-ending outa the erth.

14 Heer comes one now. A old man cuvvert with a mantell." Sol seen it was ole Sam Yell hisself, and stoop low.

15 Old Sam Yell wuz sore at bein disturbed. "Whadda ya want, braking my rest like this?" Sol sed, "I'm

sore distrest. God's gone and the Fillasteins is back. What do I do now?"

16 Sam Yell sed, "Don't ast me. If God's yer enmee you mite as well quit. It's outa yer hands now, the hole kingdum.

17 Mebbe He's give it to yer Fillastein nabers, or young Dave Id."

19 Before Sam Yell went back to his ternal rest, he terned and sed, "See ya ta-morra probly." "Where?" sez Sol. "Rite here," sez Sam Yell. "And yer sons, too."

20 Sol fell flat strait-away. Sides, he hadden eat anythin all day.

21 The witch seen he wuz in a tair-bull way.

22 She sed, "Eat sumthin, tock later."

23 Sol sed he cooden touch a thing.

24 The witch kill one of her caffs, tuck flower and kneeded it, and bake bred with it.

25 She brung it before Sol and his servints and they ate the hole thing up.

CHAPTER 29

The Fillasteins was all hopped up to do battle with Izzreal.

3 But sum of them was not so keen having Dave Id in their middest.

4 They wuz afrayed he mite tern in the middel of battel and smite them one fer his oldside.

CHAPTER 30

So the Fillasteins sent Dave Id off fer to take care of them Amalachy-ites who was enemies to both yer Fillasteins and yer Izzreal-ites.

CHAPTER 31

The Fillasteins fot and the Izzreal-ites fled.

2 They follered up on Sol's sons, and they sloo them all, incloodin Dave Id's frend, Johnnythum.

3 Sol he tuck his sord and fell on it.

4 The Fillasteins cut off his hed, strip-off his armer, and hung it up amung ther idles.

SAM YELL, TOO

CHAPTER 1

Dave Id was still beeting Amalachy-ites when he herd about Sol.

6 Oney, he was tole that Sol leened on his speer.

7 He was tole this by a Malaky-ite who claimed that Sol ast him to make shure he was ded, and this fella run him thru, and brung Dave Id Sol's crown and bracelit to prove it.

14 Dave Id ast him, "How'd you have the nerve to kill the King?"

15 And he had one of his men fall on this man till he died.

17 It was hard to tell wether Dave Id was lamentin over Sol er Johnnythum.

Sol gits his

CHAPTER 2

Dave Id ast God, "Where do I go now?" And God sed, "Heebrawn."

CHAPTER 5

When Dave Id got ther, all his tribe was waitin for him, welcummin back ther flesh and bone.

2 Dave Id becum ther King.

3 He was thirty. He rained fer the next forty yeer.

CHAPTER 6

First thing Dave Id dun was bring up the Ark of God back where it belonged.

3 They set it on a bran new cart, and brung it out of ole Abina-dab's place.

4 Everybuddy accumpneed it with mewsick, harps, cornits, simbles, and saltyrees.

6 One feller, Uzzah put his hand on it in case the oxen got it all shookup.

7 He shooden of dun it. God smote him rite there. One hit. One error.

8 Dave Id dint think the Lord shood of dun that.

9 He was nervuss bein round the Ark. And bein round the Lord too.

10 He wooden have it with him inside his own sitty of Dave Id. He let it stay in a private's home, belonging to Obeddydum the Gittite.

11 That Ark staid there three munths, and Obeddydum had a blest time thanks to the Lord.

12 So Dave Id brung the Ark outa his house and up into his place in the sitty.

13 And Dave Id made a grate sackerfice and danced in frunt of it with all his mite, and in a short skirt.

14 Sol's dotter Mickle was watchin frum a upstairs winder when Dave Id brung the Ark in with everybuddy shoutin' and him dancin, and she lothed him for it.

19 Dave Id was down there givin everywun cake and a flaggin of wine, when Sol's dotter cum up and tole him he was makin a fool of hisself in fronta all the hand-mades.

21 Dave Id sed, "This is nuthin to what I wooden do fer the Lord."

23 Mickle was barn frum that time ón.

CHAPTER 7

Dave Id now sat in a big house. He sed to Naythin his profit, "How cum I live in a seeder house, and my God lives behind curtains?"

5 That nite, God spoke to Naythin, "Mebby I shood have a house of My own.

6 Havent had one since I brung everybuddy up outa Ejippt. Sints then I've livd in tense and tabbernackles.

7 All that time I never ast My peeple to set Me up in a permamint home.

13 Let the boy bild a nice house fer his Father."

22 Naythin agreed, "Why shooden we do grate and tairible things fer You, Lord, after all You've dun fer us."

CHAPTER 9

King Dave Id still felt a bit gilty about Sol's famly. He ast if ther was enny of them left around.

2 Terned out his deer frend Johnnythum had a son lame in both feet name of Me-fib O'sheth.

7 Dave Id was happy to penshin him off fer his father's sake.

CHAPTER 10

Dave Id even felt kind tord sum of his old ennmys. He sent servints over to help out Hay Nun, king of the Aminites.

3 Them Aminitcs figgered Dave Id jist sent them over to spy on them.

4 They took them immigrunt servints of Izzreal and shave off haff thcr beerd, rip up the middel of their garmints up to thcr butticks, and sent them home.

5 Dave Id was ashame to meet them when they cum back, bein strick orthodocks, and tole them to stay over in Jerryco til ther beerds was back both sides.

6 Dave Id felt those Aminites reely stank.

CHAPTER 11

Dave Id sent his genral, Joe Ab over to take them Aminites apart, while he staid home in Jerussilem.

2 One nite he cooden sleep and was walkin the roof of his paliss when he seen this lady takin a bath. She was gorjuss, all of her.

3 He ast about her. Found it was Bath-she-bare the wife of one of his top-ades, You-ryer.

4 He tole her to cum up and see him sumtime. She did. And they did.

5 Wernt long before she tole him about a bless-it event.

6 Dave Id figgerd he better do sumthin. He sent fer Bath-she-bare's husbin.

7 Dave Id made a lotta small talk, about how the war was goin' and all, and how everybuddy was doin.

8 Then he tole You-ryer to go home, wash his feet, and Dave Id wud send him a messa meat.

9 But You-ryer dint go back to his place. He slept at Dave Id's door with all the servints.

10 Dave Id sed, "How cum?"

11 You-ryer sed, "The ark lives in a tent, that's good enuff fer me. My boss Joe Ab and my buddies is out in open fields. How can I go home and sleep with my wife under them sircumstances?"

12 King Dave Id sed: "Ritey-o. I'll git you back in them fields tomorra."

13 And Dave Id gottim drunk so's he fer shure wooden go back to his own house.

14 And Dave Id sent a letter to Joe Ab, carried by Bath-she-bare's husbin.

15 The letter sed, "See this fella don't cum back. See that he's got to the front quick and ded."

16 Joe Ab found that a eezy job.

23 A messenger brung the news of You-ryer's deth.

24 Dave Id tried to be fillasoffickle, sayin that the sord gits one as well as anuther.

25 Bath-she-bare morned her huzbin.

26 Soon's that was over, Dave Id fetched her up to the house, and they was wed. Soon's that was over, she had a son. God wernt too pleezed.

CHAPTER 12

God sent his profit Naythin to Dave Id to tell a story about the rich feller and the poor feller.

2 The richman had lotsa everythin.

3 The poorman had a little lamb. That's all.

4 Travler cumalong, wanted to buy a little lamb frum the richman. But the richman cooden be botherd dressin up one of his own so he took the poorman's little you-lamb frum him and give it to the travlin man.

5 Dave Id he was het up when he herd this story. He wanted to kill the man who had dun this.

6 "Then," sez Naythin the profit, "it's gonna be sewerside, on accounta you dun it, and you've reely dun it now, as far's God's consarned.

12 You dun it secretely but God is gonna do it to you in full vue of Izzreal."

13 Dave Id sed, "Am I gonna die?"

14 Naythin sed, "No, but yer child is."

15 Dave Id and Bath-she-bare's baby got sick. Dave Id fastid and lay all nite on the bare ground.

16 Nobuddy cud git him to git up, er eat ennything.

17 A week he lay there, and the servints was afrayed to tell him the baby was past away. They dint know what he wud do if this is the way he behave when the child was still alive.

18 But he knew alreddy. He ast if it was ded.

20 Then he got up, warsht, changed close, worshipped in the house of God, went home, and et.

21 The servints sed, "How cum you are weep-in and fast-in when the baby's still here, and when it's gone you git up and eat bred?"

22 Dave Id sed, "Wile it was alive I hoped I cud ast God to help it live.

23 Now it's ded, what can I do? I can't bring it back. May's well eat."

24 Soon after, him and Bath-shebare made anuther son called Solomon.

CHAPTER 13

Dave Id had anuther son by sumbuddy elts, call Abslalom, and a dotter, Tam-R, and anuther son by anuther muther, Am-non.

2 Am-non was sick. He love his sister Tam-R in the rong way. Amnon thot it wud be hard for him to do ennything to her on accounta she wuz a virjin. That's how sick he wuz.

3 Am-non had a frend, Johnadab, his cuzzin who musta bin sick too.

5 He tole Am-non to lie down on his bed and make hisself sick, so's his father King Dave Id wud cum to see him. The trick was to ast fer sister Tam-R to be nurse fer him.

6 Am-non dun this. He lay down, made hisself sick, and ast the King fer his sister to cum and make him a cuppla cakes rite in frunt of him.

7 So Dave Id sent home fer dotter Tam-R and tole her to whip up sum meat pies over to Am-non's place.

8 Tam-R dun what she was tole. In frunta him she rolled flour and pored the batter out.

9 Am-non wooden eat on accounta ther was too many men lookin on. So they wuz all kick out.

10 After that, Am-non ast his sister

to bring the meat into his bedroom and lettim eat offa her hand.

11 Soon as she tried to do this, he grab her and ast her to lie down.

12 His sister tole him sich things wuzn't dun, and not to cut the fool.

14 Her bruther wooden lissen and forced the issyuh.

15 After that, he hated her for what he dun. He shooda hated hisself but he took it out on her. He tole her to git up and git.

16 The poor gurl sed that bad manners like that was even worsen what he dun before.

17 Am-non call his servint fer to cum and kick er out, and lock the dores.

19 Tam-R put ashes on top of her hed, rip her virjin's dress, and balled her eyes out.

20 Her brother Abslalom herd her whaling and ast her what was up. When she tole him, he sed that was jist like a bruther and fergit about it.

21 But when dad Dave Id found out, he was roth to froth.

22 Ackshully Abslalom hated his little bruther Am-non fer doin that to ther sister.

23 He got even cuppla yeers later at a bank-wet fer sheepherders.

24 King Dave Id didden wanna go, so Abslalom ast fer young Am-non to be a guest.

26 "Why? He's not a sheeper," sed Dave Id. "Never mine," sez Abslalom.

28 Am-non cum along, and Abslalom tole his servints to lode him with wine and then knock him off.

29 Orders wuz orders. They dun it,

and it shure broke up the party.

30 Tide-ins cum back to Dave Id that Abslalom had slane all his sons, the hole passle of them.

31 Dave Id rip his close and all the servants rent thers too.

32 But his nefyew John-adab brung the strait facks. Abslalom had kill Am-non fer what he dun to Tam-R.

38 Abslalom fled aways fer three yeer.

CHAPTER 14

King Dave Id miss his son Abslalom. General Joe Ab cud see that.

23 So Joe Ab up and brung him back to Jerussilem.

24 But when he cum, King Dave Id wuden look at him. Had him took to his own place, and Abslalom never got a look-in at the paliss.

25 Too bad. Abslalom was top-to-toe the best lookin feller in the Kinkdum. Not a pimpel on him.

26 He got a hair-cut every yeer, and ther was enuff of it lyin around the barber poll fer to stuff a mattrest.

27 He had three sons, and a pritty dotter, whom he naimed Tam-R two.

28 Abslalom hung around Jerussilem fer two yeer not once seeing his father's face.

29 He kept askin Joe Ab to git his father to visit, but no dice.

30 He finely got so frust-rate he got his servints to set Joe Ab's barly feeld on fire.

31 Joe Ab sed, "Fer why did ya do that?"

32 Abslalom sed, "Why you brung me all the way home if the ole man

won't give me a look-in. Lemme see him, and if he wants to kill me, let-tim."

33 Joe Ab went to the King, Abslalom was sent fur, and you never seen sich bowin and kissin.

CHAPTER 15

Abslalom got awful poplar with the peeple.

8 He tole his father he wanted to go away agin, and do the Lord's work outta town.

9 Dave Id lettim go in piece.

10 Ackshully he was doin missyun work on his own behaff. He did a lotta poppygander about hisself and how he otta be King.

13 Dave Id herd about Abslalom makin hisself number one on the hit prade.

16 Instedda makin war with Abslalom, he and his hole homested fled, leevin behind ten konkybines fer housekeeping.

23 It look like everybuddy was heddin back to the wildernest.

24 The Ark was brung along too.

25 But Dave Id sed, "Take it back. It blongs to God. It's not on the run like us. Mebby God will bring us back sum day.

26 Let God do what He wants. He will, anyway."

37 Abslalom tuck over in Jerus-salem.

CHAPTER 16

Dave Id had his trubbles on the rode.

6 He got stoned one place by sum of Sol's old peeple.

8 They figgerd he took the job away frum Sol and put it into the hands of his boy Abslalom and served him rite, too, they sed.

9 One of Dave Id's men sed, "Why do we lissen to this ded dog? Lemme take his hed off!"

10 Dave Id sed, "Lettim curse. That's what God tole him to do."

11 But he knew that the reel curse was that the son who come outa his own bow-ills was out to git him.

12 Dave Id still hope God wud fer-giv him, as he trudged along dodjin stones and eatin dust.

CHAPTER 18

Dave Id and Abslalom finely got together. In battel.

5 The King tole Joe Ab, go eezy on my boy if you catch him.

7 It wuzn't eezy on ennybudy elts. Twenty thou was slottered in one day.

8 More peeple got it in the woods than they did in battel.

9 Abslalom was bein chase by Dave Id's men. He rid under an oak tree and his mewl went on but he didden. His hed got cot and he wuz ther swingin.

11 Sumbuddy tole Genrul Joe Ab about it.

12 Joe Ab sed, "Why dint you finsh him off? You cudda pick yourself up a few sheckles and mebby a girdle."

13 The man tole Joe Ab ther wernt enuff sheckles fer to do that after what King Dave Id tole everybuddy bout his son.

14 Joe Ab rush off to that oak and use Abslalom fer a dart-bord. He got three bullsize.

24 Dave Id was sittin with the watchman when sumwun cum run-

Dave Id takin it hard over Ab Slalom

nin up and sed, "All swell." Then he fell on his face.

25 Dave Id musta had a instink about this. He sed, "Is my boy Abslalom safe?"

26 The messinjer sed, "Everybuddy was yellin and jumpin uppendown so much I dunno what was goin on excep we won."

33 When Dave Id finely found out, he went aloan to his room and cryed his eyes out. He wisht to God he had died insted.

KINGS WON

CHAPTER 1

Dave Id was reel old now. And strickin too. Felt the cold a lot even tho he had all his cloze on.

2 His servints thot what he need fer to be in heet wuz to lie in the boozem of a young virjin.

3 They lookt around and cum up with Abby Shag.

4 She look after him good, but there wuz no hanky-panky.

5 All of a suddin, young A-denide-ya, who had cum along after Abslalom, out of Dave Id by his muther Haggis, started feeling his otes fer to be King.

6 It was nuthin his father had sed or dun. He jist felt like it.

7 And Genrul Joe Ab was helpin him too.

10 But his younger brother Solomon, was agin him. So was Naythin the profit.

11 Naythin told Solomon's muther, Bath-she-bare to tell Dave Id about this, on accounta Solomon was next in line to the throan.

15 She dun this.

20 She ast Dave Id if he minded his promiss to set her boy on the throan after him. Adding, "The eyes of Izzreal are upon you."

21 She warn Dave Id that when he slept with his fathers, a riteyuss mother like herself wud be outen the cold.

22 Naythin cum in with his two sentsworth.

24 He tole Dave Id that young A-denide-ya was goin round slotterin ox-in and fat cattel everywares and givin everybuddy free drinks so's they wud yell out, "Let's hear it fer King A-denide-ya!"

30 Dave Id sed it was fer shure Solomon was next in line.

34 He tole them that Solomon shood ride around the country blowin' his own horn and tellin everybuddy he was Kingpin.

35 Dave Id even sed he cud be King in his sted.

39 That bloo the trumpit on A-denide-ya.

47 Solomon was anointed, and even his ole dad Dave Id bow to him frum his bed.

49 Everybuddy in A-denide-ya's party left the party erly.

50 A-denide-ya was so scairt, he grab onto the horns of the alter, hopin fer sankt-you-wary.

53 Solomon brung him down offa the alter and made him promiss to be a good boy, and sent him home.

CHAPTER 2

Dave Id was goin fast.

2 He tole Solomon to look after things.

3 And fer Hevvin's sake, to walk in God's way.

6 And to be good to everybuddy, exsep possibly that ole Joe Ab.

9 "He shed so much blud around heer. I want you to shed a littel of his fer me." (FOOTNOTE: Meenin Dave Id's own blud, wich was Abslalom.)

10 Then Dave Id fell asleep with his fathers.

11 He had raincd forty yeer. Seven in Hebron, thirty three in Jerussalem.

12 Solomon tuck over.

13 His bruther A-denide-ya was like a littel lamb to his kid bruther, Solomon. He oney had one last reequess.

21 He wanted that teen-age virjin Abby-Shag, that had kept the ole King warm fer his own persnal feetwarmer.

22 Solomon, sed, "If we giv him that inch he'll want the hole Kingdum. Nuthin doin."

24 Ther was nuthin doin fer A-denide-ya after that. Next day he was fell on till he died.

25 Joe Ab knew he was next. He fled into the tabbernackle and held onto the alter horns fer deer life.

29 Solomon dint care ware he wuz. He tole a buncha peeple to fall on him.

30 But they was relucktint to do it in church, and Joe Ab wuz even more relucktint to let go of them horns.

31 But Solomon give orders.

34 Joe Ab was fell on, sloo throo and burreed in his own house which fast becum a wildernest.

CHAPTER 3

Solomon liked forn girls. He started daiting Faro's dotter, at the same time as he was bizzy bilding his own new place, the big tempel Dave Id had promisst, and a wall around the sitty of Jerussilem.

2 Peeple in them days used to sackerfice in Hy places, waitin fer that proper tempel to be bilt.

3 Solomon dun the same thing. He'd go as hy as he cud get, and burn insenst, way up there.

5 One nite, God cum to him in a dreem and ast him what he wantid most of all.

6 Solomon was strait with Him.

7 He sed he was nerviss about takin' over frum his father Dave Id, on accounta he still felt like a lil child, and didden know yet witchways was up.

9 So he ast God fer sum commonsents.

10 God liked that.

11 He said to Solomon, "You cudda ast fer longlife, er munny, er killin yer ennemies, but you ast fer branes.

12 I'm gonna put sum into you, till you'll be top of the class in ennybuddy's marks.

13 But I'm gonna give you them other things as well, as a bone-us.

14 You jist walk in my waze and keep yer nose cleen, and yule be around a longtime."

15 Solomon woke up and reelized it

was jist a dreem. But he felt a lot smarter awreddy.

16 Pritty soon, two wimmen, perfessyunal harlits, cum before him, fer to settle their squawbill.

17 Seems they live in the same house, and one of them had a baby.

18 Three days later the uther harlit had a kid too. Ther was jist the two of them livin in the house, them and ther two babees.

19 One of the little uns died in the nite, on accounta of one of the muthers rollover and squarshed it.

20 The other harlit clame that this other mother got up in the middel of the nite, while she herself was sleepin, tuck her live baby away and leff the ded one besider.

21 When she woke up fer the erly mornin feedin, she had this ded child with her, and she knew it wuznt hers.

22 The other one sed, "Yer crazy, this heer's my son which I bare."

23 Before they got to hare-pullen, King Solomon sed, "It's one harlit's word agin another's.

24 So you better take my word fer it. Bring me a sord." It was brung.

25 The king sed, "Split the differents. Give one haffa the child to the one muther, and other haff to the tother."

26 One of them wimmen let out a screem, and sed, "Oh fer hevvin's sake King, give her the hole child!" But the other sed, "Divvy it up."

27 Solomon look at the divvy-up woman and sed, "Yer not the mother. No way is a reel mother gonna be parted frum enny part of her child."

28 All Izzreal got up and applawded Solomon fer this.

CHAPTER 4

So with that, Solomon sure made hisself King over all Izzreal.

2 He rained all the ways frum the river next to yer Fillasteins up to yer boarders of Ejippt. And they all brung him presents.

31 Fer he was one wise man.

32 He turn out three thou Proverbs, and compoze mebby a thou and five hit songs.

CHAPTER 5

Even Hire'em, King of Tire, wuz a fan of Solomon's.

2 Speshully after Solomon hired Hire'm to bild his father's tempel which Dave Id had wanted to bild fer everybuddy's Father, God.

3 But Dave Id cooden do that on accounta wores on all sides.

4 But now there was peece.

6 He tole Hire'em to bild God's house outen the seeders of Lebnon, and to bring his workers too, fer everybuddy knew nobuddy cud cut it like them Lebneeze.

12 Fer once, there was peece between the two peeples as they bilt this tempel together.

CHAPTER 6

It was fore hunnert and atey yeers sints they had cum outa Ejippt that they started to bild this holey bilding.

2 It was sixty by twenny by thurty cubebs.

3 The front porch was twenny by ten.

Solomon's split dee-sizzyun

4 Lotsa winders.

7 Everythin was preepair off limits, stone cuttin and wood-hewin, so's there wooden be a lotta noisy tools wile the Lord's house was be-in bilt.

11 Word cum down to Solomon frum God.

12 God sed, "Sints you have bilt me a permamint home, Ile live with you and yer peeple ferever.

13 You keep yer word and Ile keep mine."

15 Solomon cover the stone-wirk with seeders and fur.

21 Then he overlayed the hole thing with gold.

38 The hole thing tuck seven yeer.

CHAPTER 7

Meenwiles Solomon was bilding his own house. That tuck thir-teen yeer.

2 His house was a hunnert by fifty by thirty cubebs. Much biggern God's house.

7 He had a front porch too, fer to set on and jedge peeple.

8 He also made a extry house fer Faro's dotter, whom he had taken fer wife.

9 Both houses was cuvvered with preshus stones, even in the found-ayshuns.

10 Sum of them sparkly stones wade ten cubebs.

CHAPTER 8

When it was dun, Solomon brung everybuddy together fer to deddycate the bilding, and bring up the Ark.

9 There was nuthing in the Ark but them two stone tabblets which Moeziz put there after he cum down offa the mountin and made a cuv-venant with God. But they was the cornerstones of everything.

10 As soon as the preests brung the Ark into the holey place, a cloud filled the hole house.

11 Nobuddy cud do ennything inside on accounta that cloud.

12 Solomon rememberd that nobuddy cud look on the Lord. That's why the cloud wuz there, leevin everybuddy in the dark.

CHAPTER 10

Solomon was gettin a rippitayshun as a wise man. Even over to Africker where the Queen of Shebears live.

2 She cum to Jerussalem with a grate trane, lotsa camels, carryin gold, spicys and preshus stones, and a lotta hard questyuns fer to ask Sol-omon.

3 Solomon he ansered every one.

4 She was knock out by his house too.

5 And his menyou, and what everybuddy was waring, and by the time she seen the Tempel, she had no more spearits left.

10 She give Solomon a hunnert and twenny talints, as if he hadden enuff alreddy.

11 She brung him sum all-mug trees which had never been seen in them parts.

12 Solomon used them as pillers fer the front porch of God's house, and the left-overs was made into harps and salterees.

Solomon gits old and smart

13 King Solomon give her a lotta presents in return, and she went home happy.

14 Solomon certinly kept up the gold standerd.

16 Even sheelds and targits wuz made outa gold.

17 Therd be mebby three pound a gold in one sheeld.

18 His throan was made outa ivery, overlayed with gold.

21 Everybuddy drank outa gold tumbelers. Silver didden count fer a thing in Solomon's days.

23 He was top King fer both ritches and whizdum.

CHAPTER 11

Solomon oney had one weakness. Strange wimmen.

2 God had sed, "Keep away frum forn girls, on accounta they'll git you worshipping forn gods."

3 Solomon paid no mind. He had seven hundert wives, all prinsesses, and three hundert konkybines, no bettern they shood be.

4 And shure enuff, them wives turned Solomon on to other gods, when he got old and foolish.

8 He even burnt insest in frunta them stranger gods.

9 God appeered to Solomon twicet.

10 But Solomon ignored him. God was mad.

11 That dun it. Solomon was on his way out.

29 Ther was a profit called A-hide-ya. God sent him lookin round fer a substitoot fer Solomon.

30 He found a stout young fella, Jerry Bome, all drest up in his best cloze.

31 A-hide-ya rip his new garmints into 12 peeces, and tole him to take ten.

32 Them ten peeces was simbles fer ten tribes of Izzreal. Jerry Bome was to take them over frum Solomon, leavin' him oney one, fer ole King Dave Id's sake, and last but not least, the twelfth one fer Jerus-salem's sake.

39 Meenin He was gonna afflick the seed of Dave Id. (FOOTNOTE: That'd be Solomon.) But not ferever.

40 Solomon he try to kill this Jerry Bome, who fled to Ejippt till Sol-omon was ded.

41 Nobuddy knows what Solomon did the rest of his time in offiss. Mebby God was so mad at him, nobuddy dare rite it down.

42 Solomon roold as long as his father Dave Id, forty yeer.

43 Soon as he pop off, his son Rio Bome tuck over. From then on, it wuz all downhill.

CHAPTER 12

Rio Bome went up North jist to let them know he was king of the Northerners too.

2 Meentime Jerry Bome cum back outa Ejippt.

4 The Northerners tole Rio they was sicken tired of payin fer his father's construckshun works, and wanted a tax rebait.

5 He wanted three days to think it over.

6 So he ast the old men with him what they thunk.

7 And they sed, "Give a taxcut."

8 But Rio ast the young men what they thunk.

10 They sed, "Give it to em both barls."

13 Guess who this young whippysnapper lissened to?

14 He tole the peeple, "My father Solomon give you a big yoke. You ain't seen nuthin yet. He give you whips, Ile give you scorepeons."

15 Izzreal went over to Jerry Bome.

16 The south, Joodah was stuck with Rio Bome. Everybuddy split, one way er anuther.

CHAPTER 17

Sints Kings terned out to be ded losses, peeple started lissening to profits. Like Eelyejuh the TishBite. He was a wether profit who sed they was all in fer a dry spell fer a longspell, no matter who rained at eether cort.

3 On accounta he spoke the trooth, God tole him to lie low in the dessert.

4 He lived on water and ravins' fud. God tole them birds to feed him.

6 They brung him bredcrums twice a day, plus bitsa flesh.

7 After a while, the water dride up.

9 God sent Eelyejuh to a widder woman to take care of him.

10 She was in a bad way herself, gatherin stix fer a livin.

12 When Eelyejuh ast her fer a meal, she sed she was down to her last hannfull, and a lick of oil, and she was gonna cook that fer her and her son before they laid down and died.

13 Eelyejuh ast her to bake a cake fer him first.

14 God tole him she wud never runout if she dun this.

15 Eelyejuh staid on, feeding hisself fer days and days, and she never run outa stuff.

17 But her boy got sick. So sick he was pert neer outa breth.

18 She ast Eelyejuh if it was sumthin she dun awhile back, that God wanted to take her son.

19 Eelyejuh tuck the boy up to the loft to his own bed.

20 He ast God jist what He was doin.

21 God herd, and let the boy live.

23 Eelyejuh brung him down agin and he was breething normill.

24 The woman sed, "Now I know yer the reel thing."

CHAPTER 18

It didden rane fer three yeer like God sed. So God deeside to tern the water back on.

2 He tole Eelyejuh to show hisself to King Ay Hab who wuz having a sore fam-in.

17 When Ay Hab saw Eelyejuh he sed, "So yer the trubble maker."

18 Eelyejuh sed, "No. You are. Make up yer mind who yer gonna worship. God or Bail."

19 Ay Hab wuz married to Jessy Bell, a Tire prinsess who was parshul to forn gods, so Eelyejuh sed he'd take on alla her profits, fore hunnert and fifty of them.

21 Eelyejuh tole the peeple they hadda make up ther minds to folly one or the tother, God er Bail.

23 He give the bullock test. Take two bullock, cut them in peeces, and put them on a alter with wood under but no matchez.

24 "You call on yer god, I'll call on mine, and whoever wins is God." Everybuddy agreed.

26 So the Bailmen dress up ther bullock, and kept yellin' fer Bail to cum down and start cookin. Nobuddy ansered. They even lept on top of that alter, to wake him up.

27 Eelyejuh tole them Bail was havin a long nap.

28 The Bailites wuz so frustrate they started to cut up therselfs. There was blud all over the place.

29 Nite cum and no Bail.

30 Eelyejuh took his tern. He fix up that broke-in-down alter fer the Lord.

32 He bilt a alter outa twelve-stones, one fer eech tribe.

33 He cut up his bullock, and poured fore barls of water on it.

34 He dun this three times. That's a duzzen barl. He hadda dig a trench to hold the water. Everythin was all wet.

36 Nite cum.

37 Eelyejuh ast God to do it fer him.

38 Fire cum rite down, bern up that bullock to nuthin, incloodin the wood and the stones and it even lick up all the water.

39 Everybuddy fell on ther face and sed, "That's it."

40 Eelyejuh sed, "Grab them Bail profits, and don't let enny excape." They took them down to the brook and sloo them all.

42 Eelyejuh went up to the top of Mount Caramel and pit his face tween his neeze. He wuz prayin fer rane.

43 He tole the servint to be a look-out to see what he cud see. "Nuth-in," sed the servint. Eelyejuh sent that boy seven time fer to check.

44 Finely the servint sed, "There's a bitta cloud out there, but it's no biggern yer hand." "Never mine," sed Eelyejuh. "Hitch up the charryit and go tell Ay Hab a storm is on the way."

45 It was sum storm. Eelyejuh hadda girt up his loins and run.

CHAPTER 19

Ay Hab, soakin wet, tole his wife Jessy Belle what Eelyejuh had dun with all her profits.

2 Jessy wuzn't afeerd of Eelyejuh. She sent him a note sayin that by tamorra he'd be one more profit at a loss.

3 Eelyejuh was ascairt of Jessy Belle. He run fer his life, down south to Joodah.

4 He sat down in the wildernest and ast God to let him die, feelin he wuz no bettern his fathers.

5 He slept under a jewnipper tree and a angel cum down, touch him and sed, "Time to eat."

6 He sat up, tuck sum norrishmint and lay down agin.

7 The angel tole him to have a secund helpin, fer the rode ahed.

8 That fud last him forty days and nites till he got to Mount Hoar Ebb. (FOOTNOTE: Where God first appeer to Moeziz.)

9 Eelyejuh live-in a cave. God cum and sed, "What are you doin heer?"

10 Eelyejuh sed, "I'm so disscurridge. I think I'm the oney follyer You got left."

11 God sed, "Git out and go on the mountin." Eelyejuh dun this, and

Jessy Bell goes to the dogs

along cum a big wind that brake rocks, and after that, a nerthquake. 12 After that a fire. But when God cum along He had a still small voice. 15 God tole him to git back home and on the way he'd find a miner profit to help him with his work.

19 It was young Eelye Shaw, son of Shawfat, plowing his way with a buncha oxins. Eelyejuh threw a mantel over him, and Eelye Shaw up and kwit like that.

20 He jist ast if he cud go back to the homested and kiss his pairnts goodbye. Eelyejuh sed, "Git back to yer plow. Who ast you to cum along?"

21 Eelye Shaw went back, tuck a yoke of ox-in, cook them up, and had a barby-kew. Then he went along with Eelyejuh.

CHAPTER 21

Queen Jessy Bell was still up to her old trix. Her huzbin Ay Hab had his eye on a Wine Yard blonging to a man call Nay Both.

2 Ay Hab sed, "Let's make a deel." Nay Both sed: "Nuthin doin. My old Dad wud tern over in his supple-cur."

4 Ay Hab wuz frustrate fit to bust. He lay down in his bed and wuden eat supper.

5 Jessy Belle sed, "Why're you off yer feed?"

6 He tole her about Nay Both bein stubbern. He wuden even trade Wine Yards.

7 Jessy Belle snort and say, "Whose King around heer? I'll git it for you."

8 She forge Ay Hab's name and tole sum nobles in Nay Both's town to fraim him.

10 They set up a cuppla faults witnesses clame-in that Nay Both wuz a blastfeemur.

13 They carryd him out, set him up, and stoned him till ded.

15 Jessy Belle tole Ay Hab, "See. We got that Wine Yard fer nuthin."

16 Ay Hab move in to take it over.

17 God tole Eelyejuh to move in faster.

18 And to tell Ay Hab that dogs wood be lickin his blud up in the same place as they lick up Nay Both's.

19 Ay Hab seen Eelyejuh comin and sed, "My old enmy has found me out agin."

23 God sed, "Don't fergit to menshun Jessy Belle. She's gonna end up as a dog's dinner."

27 When Ay Hab herd all that, he tore up his cloze and went home softly.

29 God sed to Eelyejuh: "He et humbel pie. Let's wate till his son's in before I lower the boom."

TWO KINGS

CHAPTER 2

Cum time fer the Lord to take Eelyejuh up with him. He sent Him down a wirlwind.

2 Eelyejuh tole Eelye Shaw to stay heer wile Eelyejuh went up ahed. But Eelye Shaw kept taggin after him.

Eelyejuh's big finish

3 The Sonsa the Profits ast Eelye Shaw if he was aware that this was the day Eelyejuh was to be took away. He sed, "Yes I know it. Hold yer peece."

4 Eelyejuh ast Eelye Shaw to stay while he went to Jerryco. But he wooden let him go alone. He tagalong to Jerryco.

5 Same thing happen when God tole Eelyejuh to hed fer Jordan. Eelye Shaw tole everybuddy to shut up and went Jordanward.

8 They got over Jordan by Eelyejuh takin off his mantell, rappin it up and smote-in the waters with it. All them waters rared up and the two profits went over dry as you pleeze.

9 Finely Eelyejuh ast Eelye Shaw why he was follying him like this. And if there was ennything he cud do fer the young fella. Eelye Shaw sed, "I'd like yer mantell and a dubble porshun of yer spearit."

10 Eelyejuh didden know if he cud manedge that. He sed, "I'm soon gonna be took away. If you see me go, you'll git what you want. If you don't, yer outa luck."

11 Down cum a charryit on fire, and horses the same way. Eelye Shaw stan back frum the blast, and Eelyejuh went up to Hevvin by wirlwind.

12 Eelye Shaw seen it all happen, and he rip his cloze off and put on Eelyejuh's mantell.

14 Cummin back over Jordan, he dun the same thing with that mantell Eelyejuh dun. He smitted the waters and never got his feet wet.

15 The Sonsa the Profits seen that, and they figgerd the spearit of Eelyejuh had cum back with Eelye Shaw.

19 Eelye Shaw went back to Jerryco and fix up the water supplye which was non-existant.

20 He jist throo sum salt in the well, and out cum fresh water.

23 On his way to Bethyl, sum little kids cum out and made fun of him fer his balled hed.

24 He fix them. He curst them and two bares cum outa the woods and tare up forty-two of them little boys. Eelye Shaw dun a lotta mirrorculls like that, but he cooden reely hold a candel to sumbuddy like Eelyejuh.

CHAPTER 24

In his day, Nabakidnestor was King of Baby Lawn.

12 He beseeched Jerussalem.

13 He carryd off outa the tabbernackel all the gold Solomon had pit in ther, and cut it up in liddle peeces.

14 He took off all the hyclass peeple too, and left the poor to shiff fer therselfs.

20 And God let it happen, fer it serfed them all rite.

CHAPTER 25

Next time he cum back, Nabakidnestor dun worse.

9 He bernt up the hole town this time.

10 The walls was broke too.

11 And he carryd off the rest of the peeple he had fergot last time.

12 Jist left a few poor beggers fer to cut the grass.

13 Tuck away all the brass this time, leff them poor peeple without a pot.

14 Not a spoon er a snuffer er a shovill was left.

24 Tole them as was remaindered to bow down to the King of Baby Lawn and they'd git by.

FIRST AND SECOND CROCKANICKLES

This is a rehash of what has gone before.

THE BOOK OF EZZRER

CHAPTER I

Sire-us of Purseya took over where Nabakidnestor left off when he died.

2 Sire-us proclame hisself lord hinemitey everything, and sed God tole him to bild him a house at Jerussalem.

CHAPTER 3

So the childern of Izzreal what had been fudgitives in Baby Lawn fer a dog's age, got reddy to git back to the old home.

2 They was reddy to offer up bernt offrins agin, mornin, noon anite.

6 But the Tempel back home didden even have a foundayshun enny more.

7 They got a grant frum Sire-us fer to reebild.

CHAPTER 4

The enmys of Joodah herd about the childern of cavativity cummin back and rebildin the Tempel.

2 They offert to help and sed they sot the Izzreal God too.

3 Zerobabble the Izzreal leeder sed, "Nuthin doin."

4 So these strangers hung around and trubbled the work, doin ther best to frustrate. And rote letters to complane.

5 This happen all thru the rain of Sire-us, and Dairy-us, (FOOTNOTE: Anuther king of Pursya.)

6 And A-has-you-wereas.

7 And Artaxirksus.

10 And even the grate Asnapper who had took over Sumarea.

11 Heer's a tippicle letter.

12 "Them Jews which has cum back is rebilding this bad sitty frum the foundayshuns uppard.

13 If they do it, and set up ther walls agin, then lookout. You won't git a sent of tribewt outa them."

18 The king rit back: "I had yer letter red before me.

19 I check the old-time files and

found that this sitty was revolting a longtime.

21 So stop work immeejitly and unbild this sitty. Yers, Artaxirksus."

24 Ther was a big work stoppedge.

CHAPTER 5

Sumbuddy membird the deecree that Sire-us of Pursya had made.

15 He had sed it was awrite to go ahed with the work.

CHAPTER 6

Dairyus, the present encumbrence of Pursya, made a deecree to tryn find Sire-usses deecree.

2 They found a roll with a reckerd in it.

3 It sed let God's house be bilt,

sixty cubebs hy and sixty wide.

5 And let all them vessles wich Nabadkidnestor took be put back.

11 Whoever alters this word, let the timbers be shiverd down frum his house, and tern into a dunhill.

12 Ther was a lotta shiverd timbers in Jerussalem that nite, and a lotta bilding too.

CHAPTER 10

Ezzrer tole everybuddy that they had cum to a pritty trespass aginst ther God, and married pritty strange wives.

3 Time to make a new Cuvvenant with God, and start by putting away all them forn-born wives, not to menshun the kids too.

THE
BOOK OF NEERMYER

CHAPTER 1

The Tempel was bilt but the walls was still broke-in-down and the gates was bernt.

CHAPTER 2

Neermyer work fer Artaxirksus over to Pursya. He was his wine-stoord.

2 The king sed, "I'm sick at hart about my hometown which is a pritty rundown place."

6 King Artaxirksus sed, "Go fix it up. When will you be back?"

7 Neermyer set him a time, and went.

CHAPTER 4

The wall wuz startin to bild up when sumbuddy name Sandball-Lot took offence at the idee.

2 He sed, "Are we gonna let these feeble Jews fortyfy therselfs?"

3 His frend Toe-buyer laffed and sed, "Lissen, with that wall they're bildin, if a fox jumps on it, it'll fall down."

6 But the peeple had a mind to work, and Neermyer was a good orgynizer.

8 Sandball-Lot and Toe-buyer was prepaired to fite the wall, so Neermyer figgerd the Jews shood fite back.

16 Haff the peeple worked and the other haff was on watch, with speers and sheelds.

18 Even the bilders had sords at ther side.

23 They work nite and day, and nobuddy ever took ther cloze off sept on wash-in day.

CHAPTER 5

Ther was sum grumblin amung the richer agin the poorer.

2 They had grubsteak the workers on the wall with corn.

3 A lotta them had put up morgidges fer to buy that corn, and borried munny fer to pay tribewt to the Purzyin King.

5 They wundert if the hole wall thing was worth it.

6 Neermyer got hot and tole them off.

7 He rebewk the morgidge-holders fer taken sich interest outa ther own brethern and sistern.

11 He sed that all detts wud be cansell so that everybuddy wud start out agin even.

12 Everybuddy took an oaf and promisst.

13 Neermyer got up and shook his lap, and sed ennybuddy who didn't cooper-rate wud be simlerly shook up.

14 Tuck him twelve yeer to rebild that wall.

16 And he never made a red sent out of it.

CHAPTER 8

Fer the offishul openin of the Wall, everybuddy gatherd at the old Water Gait.

2 Ezzrer red the law to them, jist like Moeziz laid down.

18 It was a ate-day party follyed by a solm one-day affair.

CHAPTER 9

The ate-th day they all cum in sackedcloth, cuvvered in erth, with nuthin to eat.

CHAPTER 11

Here was the rools. The roolers was to live in Jerussilem. The rest of the peeple was to cast lots. One in ten was to live inside the sitty, the other nine was stuck in the stix.

2 The peeple blest everybuddy willin to stay inside Jerussalem.

CHAPTER 13

When they laid down the law of Moeziz, they memberd that he had sed no Ammnites or Moe-Bites aloud in the congergayshun.

19 The Sabbith was kept agin. The town gates was shut weekends at sundown, and not open till after. Servints was set on the walls fer to make sure no trade went on.

20 A lotta merchints hungaround outside the walls Sardys and Sundys hopin fer breeches. (FOOTNOTE: In the law, wernt no more breeches in the new wall.)

21 Neermyer skeered them all away by threttnin them with the layin on of hands.

23 There was a lotta Jews had married out-of-town wimmen.

24 Ther kids spake haff-forn and sum of them cooden unnerstan Yiddish.

25 Neermyer smoat sertin of

these, pluckoff ther hare, and made them sware not to do it agin.

26 That's what Solomon did. What cozz all the trubble in the firsplace, was these outlandish wimmen he tuck up with.

THE BOOK OF ESTOR

CHAPTER 1

This happen in the days of Ah-as-you-wereas, who rained frum Injure all the way over to Eethy-why-opia. That'd be over a hunnert an twenny seven provinsez.

2 He sat on the throan in his paliss in Shooshan.

3 Third yeer out, he give a big feest fer all his help, prinses and servints, Meeds and Purshins.

4 He shoad off all his ritches fer haff a yeer. It was sum blast.

5 After the ball was over, he throo a liddel post-party fer the help in his paliss.

6 It was a cullerfull do. Hangins in green, white and bloo fassened with purpull cords, gold and silver beds on pavemints of red, bloo, blacken wite marbels.

7 The wine was in gold goblins and fload like wine shood.

8 Nobuddy hadda drink if they didden wanna. You did what you wanted as long as you dun what yer tolled.

9 Eekwal time too. Queen Vashty give a simmler party fer the wim-men.

10 But the king wanted the queen over to his party fer to show off her bewdy.

11 She wooden cum. The king got roth.

15 He ast the wisemen what he shood do with her.

17 They tole him it made him look bad to other huzbins.

18 And not much good among contemptuary wimmen eether.

19 "Kick Queen Vashty out and give her job to sumbuddy elts," they sed.

20 "That'll put wimmen in ther place."

21 The king like this ideer.

22 He sent letters off to everybuddy in them 127 provinshuls, that man is boss in the house.

CHAPTER 2

So Vashty was give the boot.

2 Next thing was to git sum young virjin to replace her.

3 Then begun the roundup fer the bewdy contest.

4 The winner got to be Mrs. King.

5 Morty Ky was a Jew workin in the Shooshan paliss.

6 He had bin carryd away frum Jerussalem by Nabakidnestor.

7 He had brung up Estor, a liddle orfin, on accounta he was her unkel, relativly speeking. She was a looker.

8 He got Estor to join the cattel-call of pulkertewd.

13 Every girl was to cum before the king and cum back the next mornin. She hadda report back to Shash-gash, the Yewnick in charge of kon-kybimes.

14 That's all unless she got a call-back frum the king.

16 Estor won hands down.

17 He cooden wate to crowner.

18 Ther was anuther big feest.

19 Oney Morty Ky knew his nees was Jewish. He tole her to keep it to herself.

21 Morty Ky used to sit by the king's gait, so he pritty well knew what was goin on. He overherd a cuppla chamberlanes of the King, Big Than and Tairash plottin agin ther souverin.

22 He tole Estor, and she tole the King what Morty Ky had tole her.

23 Both them thugs end up hung.

CHAPTER 3

King A-has-you-wereas appoint Hayman to be topman in his paliss.

2 Everybuddy bow down to Hayman, sept Morty Ky.

5 This burn Hayman sum, speshully when Morty Ky was a Jew.

6 Hayman figgerd if he got rid of all Jews that'd solve the Morty Ky problim.

8 He tole the King ther was a sertin bunch of refugees hangin around, and they was differnt frum uther peeple, and didden keep the king's laws.

9 He ast the King permissyun to destroy all of them. It wooden cost all that much.

10 The king tuck off his ring, give it to Hayman fer a sine to go ahed.

11 "Do with them peeple as seems good to you."

12 Hayman drew up a progrom and the King sined it.

13 It sed to deestroy, kill and cozz to pairish all Jews, yungun old

incloodin littel childern and wimmen, all in one day, the thirteenth of the munth. Ennything took off them wud be fair pray.

15 After the king sined, Hayman and him had a drink. But the hole sitty of Shooshan was rot up about this.

CHAPTER 4

Morty Ky he rent his cloze and went out and cryed.

2 He hedded up fer the kings gait but he cooden git in, bein a Jew.

3 In all 127 provinsees, ther was whaling and nashing and mourning over this.

4 Estor was tole about Morty Ky. She sent cloze out to cuvver him but he wooden take them.

5 Estor sent a note to ast him why.

8 Morty Ky sent back Hayman's deecree, and tole her to supple-cate the King.

11 Estor rit back to Morty Ky that if the King hold out his gold-in septer, he lives no matter who trys to put him to deth.

13 Morty Ky cum back with "Better git the King to holdout. Yer a Jew too, and nobuddy excapes.

14 Mebby you were chose jist fer this. Don't hold yer peece."

15 Estor rit back:

16 "Git all the Jews together, fast fer three days. Likewise me and my maidins. Then I go to the King, even if it's agin the law. If I don't make it, I don't make it."

CHAPTER 5

Estor put on all her trap-ins and got reddy to meet the King.

2 When the king seen her, she was a knockout. He held out his royal gold septer to her. She droo neer, and touch the tip of it.

3 "What kin I do fer ya, Estor my queeny. I don't care if it's haff my kingdum."

4 Estor sed, "All I want is to give you a good dinner, and let Hayman cum to the bankwet too."

5 "De-lited," sed the King.

9 Hayman was pleeze to be invit. But when he past the gate ther was Morty Ky sittin ther payin him no respeck. Hayman was neer appleplexy.

10 But he refraned hisself fer the momint, and went to visit frends.

11 Where he tole them what a magniffisint purson he was, and how well he was bein permoted by the king abuv everybuddy elts.

12 He menshun that Queen Estor had invit him aloan to dine with the King.

13 But he nashed his teeth over Morty Ky. "I get no respeck."

14 His frends tole him to make a gallows fifty cubans hy, and ast the King to git Morty Ky to swing frum it. Hayman thot that was a gud joke.

CHAPTER 6

King A-has-you-wereas cooden sleep that nite. He sat up in bed reeding the Crockanickles.

2 It tole ther about Morty Ky savin his life frum Big Thana and Tairash.

3 He thot, "What have we dun fer Morty Ky?" He look it up. "Not a thing."

4 Next day Hayman cum to him.

6 Before he cud speek to the king about them gallows, the king ast Hayman what shood be dun fer a man the king wanted to honner. Hayman figgerd the king was tockin about hisself.

7 So Hayman sed:

8 "Nuthin but the best. Let all the king's second-hand cloze be brung, and his horse too, and why not the crown fer his hed? Let all this be deliverd by hand, and bring him on horseback throo the streets of the sitty, and proclame what a grate man he is."

10 The king sed, "Good. Do all that fer Morty Ky sittin at the gate. Don't fale."

11 Hayman must have bust a blud vessle doin this. When he got dun he went home and cuvvered his hed in morning.

14 He wuz reeminded to cum to that bankwet tonite.

CHAPTER 7

All three shoad up fer the bankwet, the King, Hayman and Estor.

2 In the middle of the wine, the king sed, "Estor mine, whadda ya need? Like I sed, haff the kingdum an it's yores."

3 "Sints you ast," sed Estor, "how bout my life and my peeples?

4 We are all soled to be slane. If it was jist fer slaverey it wooden be so bad, but this is so permamint."

5 The king ast, "Who dares to slay you, my deer?"

6 "That Hayman ther, the wicket purson," sed Estor. Hayman felt it wuz time to leeve.

Estor gits Haymon all hung up

7 The king was so mad he hadda go out in the garding fer a bit.

8 When he cum back Hayman was on Estor's bed, and so was she. Sed the king: "Are you tryna force things rite heer in my house?"

9 The king felt better when Hayman wuz hung on his own gallows.

THE BOOK OF JOBE

CHAPTER 1

There was this man in the land Oz, name of Jobe. He was absolootly purfick.

2 He had seven sons and three dotters.

3 Pluss seven thou sheep, three thou cammel, 500 yokedoxin, 500 she-ass. He was the biggest man in the eest.

4 Life was all feesting at sumbuddy's house er other.

5 Jobe he was up gooden erly, makin extry sackerfices in case anybuddy in the famly had a sin they fergot about.

6 God was lookin at this bunch one day, when Saytin cum along.

7 "Speek of yerself," sed God. "What brings you up heer?" Saytin sed, "I like walkin around and uppen down."

8 God sed, "Yule git no bizness frum my obeejunt servint Jobe. He's a dandy."

9 Saytin laffed and sed, "What's he got to worry about?

10 Ya hedge him in on allsides, ya set him up so's he cant looze.

11 But turn agin him, and he'll morn likely spit in Yer Face."

12 It was God's tern to laff, "Try him. Jist try. Only no persnal dammidge, understan?" Saytin went down to try his trix.

13 He pick a day when all Jobe's sonsandotters was havin' a feed and a drink over to ther elder bruther's place. Saytin went to work.

14 First sum servint cum up and tole Jobe that his oxes and his asses was fell upon by a buncha outlanders.

15 They sloo all the servints as well (sept the servint who was tellin him all this).

16 Anuther servint cum up a runnin and tole about flaims fallin frum Hevvin that bernt up the sheep. And wuz the servints ever bernt up too. (Sept him left to tell the tail.)

17 More bad noos. A band of bad'uns fell on the camels, carted them off, but not before slooin' off alla the camel servints.

18 If that wernt enuff, sumbody cum frum where the houseparty was goin on.

19 Sum wind cum wippin outa the wildernest and flatten the house, and everybuddy inside went flat too.

20 That dun it. Jobe got up, tore his sheet in two, give his hed a beanshave, and fell down to pray.

21 He sed, "I now got what I started out with at berth. I'm even. God gimme, and God takes back. Bless Him, ennywaze."

CHAPTER 2

Ther was anuther Angels' meetin up in Hevvin and Saytin cum along to heckel.

3 God sed, "What do you think of my boy Jobe, after all you dun to him?"

4 Saytin sed, "I dun nothin' to him personal. You wooden let me.

5 Lemme git under his skin, that's a differnt story."

6 God sed, "I leeve him on yer hands."

7 The Devil found work fer his idol hands. They cuvver Jobe top to toe with boyles.

8 Jobe got so itchee he finely end up scraypin hisself with a old peesa pot.

9 Mizziz Jobe cum out and nag him, "What are you sittin ther scratchin fer? Shake yer fist up at Him that dun this, then lay down and kwit."

10 Jobe tole her she was talkin like a ninny. "Do you expeck it alwaze to be a bed of flours? Take the bidder with the swede."

11 Jobe had three friends herd about his tuff luck. Eliphantz, Bill Dad, and So-far. They cum to say "Tich tich, ain it a shaim."

12 They all dun the rite things . . . weepin, rentin mantels, and heepin dert on ther heds.

13 They sat up with him 7 nites and nobuddy sed a word. They didden have to. They seen what a mess he was.

CHAPTER 3

Finely Jobe opened his mouth to sware.

3 "I wish life was rettero-activ and I cud fergit all about been borne. Er even conseeved.

4 Wipe this one outa the calender.

10 I wisht my muther's woom had bin shut up that day.

11 I shooda give up the goast when I cum outa that belly.

17 I wanna take the Long Rest."

CHAPTER 4

Eliphanz felt he hadda speek.

3 "Jobe, you was alwaze a kwik one with the Advice.

5 Now it's yer tern.

7 You mustov hadda dun sumthing to deserf this.

8 Sich things don't happen fer nuthin.

17 Mebby it's fer bein holeyer than thou. Or in this case, Him."

CHAPTER 5

Trubble is everybuddy's middel name. Axcept it.

17 You shood be happy that God is takin time fer to correck you.

27 He's probly doin this fer yer own good."

CHAPTER 6

Jobe had a anser, "If you had this rash you wooden tock so cam.

4 God has got his arrers into me, and tip them with poysen.

5 Yer wild ass don't bray when he's bizzy eetin grass. Yer ox don't kick his stall out, long's he's got his fodder.

7 But I bin rejuiced to one big itch.

8 I jist ask oney one thing of God.

9 Fer to let go and cut me off.

10 That wud do me dandy.

14 Yer sposed to be my friend Eliphanz. Wher's yer piddy?
27 You sound like yer diggin a pit fer me.
30 Jist go back home, will yuh?

CHAPTER 7

My time is cum. I kin see that.
5 I'm dusty and fulla werms and scabs. My skin is absolootly roar.
6 Everytime I pickit I brake out agin.
7 Life is jist a bag of wind to me.
12 But who ast you fellers to keep watch over me like a beeched wail?
13 Leeve me alone to swaller my spiddle.
20 As fer you, God, what did I do to You?
21 And if I did sumthin, why can't You parden it? And hurry, I'm not gonna be heer long. Pleez git offa my back."

CHAPTER 8

Bill Dad, the Shoo-Hite sed:
2 "What a lotta guff yer tocking!
3 Do you think God is ever rong?
4 Mebby yer kids dun the sin and that's why they was cutoff.
6 Sumbuddy musta dun sumthin. Utherwise God wooden have dun this.
7 You started out small, but you made it big fast.
9 But what's the differents in a hunerd yeers?
20 If you wuz blaimless, God wooden rejeck you.
21 You'd be laffin and woopin and hollerin. Stedda weepin and whalin!"

CHAPTER 9

Jobe cooden wate to anser Bill Dad:
3 "You think I wanna cumpeat with God? Tell him what to do?
4 Nobuddy's every tryed that and got away with it.
5 He knocks off mountings that git in his way.
6 He gives everything the shakes.
7 He tells the sun wether to git up or not, and tells the stars when to shut up fer the nite.
11 I cant even see Him, but He kin see me.
12 So who is goin to say to Him: "What are You doin?"
14 He don't anser to nobuddy.
15 I wooden know how to anser Him, even tho I am innersent. Guess I better jest apeel fer mersey.
19 All the mussle is on His side. He don't need enny jedgement frum me.
20 I'm not guilty, but I cooden open my mouth without pudden my foot in it.
22 Besides, He knocks off yer gilty and yer not gilty.
24 Sumbuddy puts the blinds on justiss. If not He, who?
27 If I say, Ile fergit about it and don't complane, yule all think I'm gilty, rite?
30 You fellers wud say black wuz white ennywaze.
32 I don't expeck enny sitch jedgement frum God.
33 A jedge is jist a man in a cort.
34 If He'd put down His rod, I cud pleed with Him."

CHAPTER 10

That's why I wanna git this hole thing over with. I'm not gonna holed back. I admit I'm bidder.

2 I'll tell God, 'Stop pickin on me till you tell what I dun rong!'

3 Duz it make Him feel good doin sumthin like this?

4 Duz He have enny ideer what all this feels like?

7 Even tho' He knows I dun nuthin?

8 God, you started me. Now it looks like yer tryna finish me off.

9 You made me outa clay, and now Yer workin to grind me down to dust.

10 You pored me out like milk. Now Ya curdel me like cheeze.

11 'Twas You put skin on my flesh, and knit my boans and sinyous.

18 Why did Ya go to all that trubble in the furse place?

19 I shooda gone strait to the graiv frum the woom.

20 How much time I got left? Let's fergit it. Cumfert me by leeving me aloan."

CHAPTER 11

Then upspeek So Far the Namath-Ite.

2 "Jobe, I'm not gonna let you git away with all that blather. Tockin' that way is not gonna git you offen the hook.

3 You think I'm gonna sit heer wiles you spout off all them fibs?

4 You sed you was cleen. Shure, in yer own eyes, mebby.

5 But how good wud you look if God reely spoke-up?

6 Mebby He's bin takin it eezy on you. Mebby you deserf werse!

8 Yer outa yer depf with God, Jobe.

9 Whadda you know?

16 Fergit yer mizzrys.

20 Give up and reepent."

CHAPTER 12

Jobe was berning with morn his boyls.

2 "Arnt you the ones! Won't be no whizdum left after yer bunch is gone!

3 Lissen, I'm as smart as enny one of youse.

24 I know you cant expeck no bedda rozes."

CHAPTER 13

I know, I'm the one who's lyin in it.

2 So don't tell me I dunno what you know.

3 After lissenin to yew three, I'm reddy fer sumthin bigger. I'd ruther talk to Him, and git sum rimer reeson outa this.

4 Fine buncha bedside dockters you three tern out to be.

5 Best thing you kin do is shut up. Fer you that wud be whizdum.

9 He mite cum lookin fer you three sumday.

10 And He'll tare a strip offa you fer what you sed today.

14 Ile take my chantses with Him rite now. What elts kin I do?

18 I've figgerd out what to say, and I know Ile win my case.

20 God, I oney ask two things. 1) Take Yer hevvy hand offa me and 2) don't let me be too scairt of You.

21 If You call, Ile anser.

22 Or lemme speek first, and then You anser.

23 Let me know what I dun rong, and how much.

141

CHAPTER 14

Us yueman beans don't git long to hang around. That's life. Short time, big problms.

2 You soon clip us down like a dandylion.

3 I sumtimes wonder if You notiss sich things. You can't bring evry little thing to jegemint.

6 Why don't You look away sumtimes and let the poor dog have his day?

7 Now trees is differnt from peeple.

8 Cut them down, don't matter, they got furm roots.

9 After a little rane, they start shootin up agin.

10 But man oney gits one shot at it.

12 He falls and don't git up again.

13 There's no garntee he'll ever live everafter.

19 Like a rock, he gits granually wore down to grit.

20 Duz he ever know if his oftspring that suckseeds him comes to enny good er not?

22 By that time, he's awreddy under fer the count."

CHAPTER 15

Eliphanz chip in his bit agin.

2 "I dunno wether it's werth answerin Jobe or not. He's jist fulla eestwind.

4 The ideer! Tryna git around the feer of God!

5 Watever sin you dun, Jobe, yer jist tryin to git around it.

6 Yer own lips is testy-fyin agin you.

7 You think yer oldern the hills?

8 Do you have the minits of God's Meetins? Are you the oney wiseman around?

10 You should alwaze lissen to men old enuff to be yer father.

13 You otta be ashame tockin the way you do.

15 God don't even truss his saints, let alone them angels.

16 Why should he truss a dirty littel man like you?

18 How menny times have we bin tolled. . . .

20 It's the wicket what rithes in pane all the time.

21 On accounta they has rared up agin God,

22 And Dee-a-fide the Almitey.

34 Whoe beetide sich!

35 They conseeves mischiff, brings fourth eevil, and ther belly preepairs deseat."

CHAPTER 16

Jobe had his tern agin.

2 "What mizzerbull comferters you make! You make me shivver.

3 When are you gonna run outa steem?

4 I cud spout off like you, if you wuz in my place.

5 Its eezy to shaik yer hed at sumbuddy elts.

7 I don't need you three to ware me out. God has seen to that.

9 All yer nashin and gashin is in vane, God got ther ferst.

10 Then He hand me over to my fella yewman beans.

11 They carried on His werk.

12 I wuz doin fine, till He grab me by the neck like a chickin.

13 Slash open my kidnees, and pore my gaul on the ground.

Jobe gits little help frum his frends

17 Me, what have I dun back? Notta thing.

21 I wud like the chants to tock this over with Him."

CHAPTER 18

Bill Dad the Shoo-Hite kept at him:

2 "How long you gonna keep this up?

4 You think He's gonna make a eggsepshun of you?

8 Yer trippin on yer own feet, if you ast me."

CHAPTER 19

Jobe ast him:

2 "How long you gonna keep at me?

3 Ten times now you bin yammerin at me. You got no shaims?

4 If I had aired, witch I never, it's my bizness, it's my airer.

6 But I dint. God has put me in the rong.

7 And He won't anser me back.

13 Everybuddy is agin me now.

14 Incloodin my kinfoke.

16 The servints snub me.

17 The wife finds me reepulsif.

18 Younguns gimme no respeck.

19 Frends stay away in droves.

20 All I got left is the skin of my teeth.

23 I wisht sumbuddy wud rite this all down in a book.

26 I know the wurms are gonna get me, and after that Ile see my Maker.

27 I'm nerviss about that.

29 But we all cum to Jedgemint."

CHAPTER 20

So Far sed:

2 "I gotta hurry up and anser that.

5 The trumpetin' of the wicket will be short.

6 You may git yer head in the clouds fer a seckund,

7 But yule last about as long as yer own stool. Everybuddy's gonna look around and say: 'Whair'd he go?'

11 Yer boans, witch is fulla the sinsa yer yooth, will lie down with you.

12 You can't hide wicketness with the sweetness of yer tung.

13 Evil taists sweet. Ya hate to let it go, so you holed it in yer mouth,

14 Till it terns yer stummick.

15 You kin swaller ritches but you'll throw them up agin,

28 Becuz all yer goods has floan away on the Rath of God.

29 That's what a wicket man gits, and serfs him rite."

CHAPTER 21

Jobe spoke back.

2 "Now heer me good.

3 Bare with me, before you run me down agin.

7 I see wicket peeple reeching old age. Fulla power. Safe as houses.

9 They got no rod of God on them.

14 They tell God to git away frum them. Lettum be!

15 Who needs You!!

16 And do they suffer fer it? No sirree!

17 How menny wicket lamps have you seen snuffout?

19 You say God is jist layin in wate fer them.

23 But when they pass on, ther all wrap in gold,

24 Body all fat, boans still moyst, and

25 Next to a fella in a popper's grave never had a square meal.

26 But it's all the saim when the wurms git at them."

CHAPTER 22

Eliphanz the Termite sed:

3 "Do you think God likes you bean so self-ritechuss?

4 You think it duz Him good to heei how blaimless you are?

5 Ile bet you bin a grate sinner in yore day.

9 Sendin' widders and orfins away emty-handed. Things like that.

13 How kin you say: 'What does God know?'

21 You better humbull yerself.

29 God knocks down prowed ones like you. You better git loaly.

30 And make sure yer hands are cleen."

CHAPTER 23

Jobe groned and sed:

3 "Ide like to find Him.

4 Ide put my case in fronta Him.

5 He'd anser me.

7 And I bet Ide get off.

10 He knows where I am, but I can't find Him ennywares.

11 I bin tryna dog His footsteps all my life.

15 Mind, don't think I'm not scairt of Him.

17 I know He keeps me . . . But He keeps me in the dark."

CHAPTER 24

Why don't God do sumthin about everythin that's rong?

3 Mite is rite everyware.

4 Poor peeple gits kicked around.

12 God don't seem to pay them no mind.

14 Merder is gittin more poplar.

15 Adulterrors is bizzy every day. Or every nite.

18 Yet you three say 'the wicket git theirs.'

22 Seems to me God don't hinder them at all.

23 If ennything, they gits it eeziern most."

CHAPTER 25

Old Bill Dad give a anser to this'un:

2 "Lissen man, we is all maggits, and our sons is wurms."

CHAPTER 26

Jobe sed, "Thanksa lot. Jumpin' on a man when he's down.

4 Who gives you them ideers?

14 We kin see and heer with our eers how all-pourfull He is, And we only git a small wisker of it.

15 But who kin figger out what His thunder is sayin?"

CHAPTER 28

Us men cuvvers the erth, and digs under it, and finds everythin.

12 Eggsept whizdum.

13 Man doan know whair to look fer it.

23 Oney God has the key.

28 The oney whizdum we got is our feer of the Lord."

CHAPTER 29

I shure wisht," Jobe went on, "that I wuz like I wuz before.

12 I wuz good to widders and orfins.

17 Tuck care of the wicket too, by brakin ther teeth fer them. Makin them drop ther ill-got-in gaines.

18 In them days I thot Ide die in my nest multyplyin like the sands on the beech.

20 I had it made.

21 Everybuddy wud shut up till I finisht tocking.

23 They wated with ther mouths open like I was spring rane.

24 I give everybuddy a smile and that smile give everybuddy confidense.

25 I was king of the cassel in them days.

CHAPTER 30

Now I'm the joker in the pack. Everybuddy's discard.

19 God has throne me on the man-oorpile of life.

CHAPTER 31

I wonder if God has kept track of all my steps?

6 Ile stand on my reckerd.

7 Look me up in the books.

16 If ther's one black mark agin me,

22 Let my shoulders fall off and my arm be broke frum the sock-it.

27 If I have bin over-prowed in enny way, even lettin my mouth kiss my own hand,

29 Or gloted over my ennymees,

33 Or hid any deelings frum ennybuddy....

35 I jist want a fare heering, is all.

37 I've kep track of everything." Jobe run out of words.

CHAPTER 32

And Jobe's three 'frends' finely clam up too.

2 Then a young fella, Elly Hoo, the Buzzite suddinly got up mad. He had bin sittin in on all this. He wuz mad at Jobe tryna justyfy hisself.

3 He wuz mad at Jobe's frends cuz they tole him he was rong but never tole him why.

4 Elly Hoo was a young tad, that's why he wated fer to speek.

5 That didden make him any less mad.

7 He figgered, let the seenyer sittizens have ther say, and mebby Ile lern sumthing.

9 "But old don't make wize," Elly Hoo sed.

10 "So gimme my tern.

11 I wated fer you three to do it.

12 I give my undivide attenshun to yer drivvel.

19 I bin holdin back fit to bust."

CHAPTER 33

I'm saim as the rest of you, rite? Commin clay.

7 You don't needa be ascairt of me.

8 But I herd you say, Jobe,

9 That yer cleen.

10 And God is jist bein picky

11 Tryna find sumthin aginst you.

12 Yer not rite you know. You gotta reelize this. God is greater than yew.

13 What do you fite Him for?

14 What kinda anser do you expeck frum Him? You and Him don't tock the same langridge.

16 He mite tock to you in a dreem. That's when He mite open yer eers.

17 But that's jist a warnin to step back frum the Pit.

18 He's tryna save yer mizzerbull life, is all.

24 He's lookin fer a ransum fer you.

25 He wants to bring the blume back to yer cheeks.

27 Jist say yer sorry.

28 And you'll git outa the pit and see the lite.

CHAPTER 34

Jobe clames he's innersent.

9 He feels he's got a raw deel by God.

10 As if God is the wicket one.

12 The Lord don't do things like that.

18 Wud you go up to a king and tell him he's wicket?

19 Well, Jobe, that's what yer doin to God.

24 Yer reely askin fer trubble.

31 You shood jist tel Him, I've bin punisht and I won't do it agin.

37 You ain't only bin in sin, you bin rebellyuss too.

CHAPTER 35

Do you think it's rite to say that yer riter than Him?

13 Tock about vane, now that's vane. I don't blame God fer not lissening.

16 All yer gum-bumpin has bin fer nuthin.

CHAPTER 36

Sints He's not heer, I'm gonna speek on God's behaff.

3 First of all I'm gonna give Him the bennyfit of yer dout. He's riteyuss.

4 And I'm tellin you strait. He's on yer side.

5 He don't hate nobuddy.

6 But He don't exackly help the wicket; insted He gives to the poor.

7 He treets the ritechuss like kings, and has them eggsalted.

9 If they go rong, He shows them.

10 Thunders in ther eer to dissaplin them.

11 If they kwoperate they do fine.

12 But lookout if they don't.

17 You look pritty wicket to me, Jobe.

18 You cud be took off at a stroke.

26 Don't try to figger Him out. Jist kwopperate.

CHAPTER 37

Lissen to Him and lissen good.

4 He's not hard to heer.

5 He's got a big voice,

6 Tells the wether what to do.

12 He's in charge of everything.

14 You better stanstill and look around ya.

15 Do you know how all this stuff got here?

23 This isnt a riddel, cuz there's no anser.

24 Whizdum meens nothin to Him."

CHAPTER 38

All of a suddint a big Wind wirl up. God step out of it and sed:

2 "Who was that iggerammus who was jist tocking?

3 Get reddy, Jobe. Now I'm askin the kwestyuns.

4 Ware wuz you when I started this hole thing?

5 Who drop the first plum line?

6 What's it all fassened to? Did you lay the cornerstone

7 That day when we had the openin sairymoanies?

8 Who makes the Tide tables fer the sea?

12 Who wakes the sun up?

16 Have you checkt out the deep bottom of the sea?

21 You know all this, don't you, becuz you were around when it started!

CHAPTER 40

Well, faltfinder, you wanta square-off with Me?"

2 And Jobe sed, "Who am I to anser You?"

6 So God went on:

8 "So you wanta put Me in the rong, jist so you can justyfie yerself.

16 Lookit that monster, Bee-Hee Moth. (FOOTNOTE: This is God's name fer a HyppyOptimus.)

19 Fackt is, I made him before I made you.

CHAPTER 41

What about Lee Vye-athan. (FOOTNOTE: Pet name fer a crockydial.)

8 I wuden advize you try ennything with this feller!

9 I seen men faint at the site of him.

11 Him and everythin else under Hevvin is mine.

13 He's got a dubble coat of male plates.

14 Anybuddy care to open the dubble dores to his face?

18 When he sneezes, lites flash,

19 Flames cum leepin out.

20 Smoke belchiz out of his nosterills.

25 When he rizzes up even the mitey are afrayed.

26 Sords don't meen a thing to him.

27 Arn is jist like straws agin him.

28 Arrers, slingshots, clubs, and java-lines all make him laff.

31 When he thrashes the sea boils like a pot.

32 With a shiney wake behind.

33 Nuthin on erth like him. Absolootly feerless.

34 King of the pride brigaid."

CHAPTER 42

Jobe finely spoke up:

2 "I know what you kin do, and there is no goin aginst You.

3 I had no idee what I was tocking about.

5 I had herd a lot about You, but now I see You fer the first time.

6 I feel like a fool. I'm sorry."

7 Then God terned to Jobe's so-call frends, espeshully Eliphanz the Termite: "I am reely fed up with the three of you. My servint Jobe spoke rite, but you never did.

8 You three git seven bullsanrams and put up a bernt offrin. Jobe will leed the prairs for you, so's I won't give you what you reely deserf."

9 This they all dun.

10 After prairs, God brung all Jobe's stuff back, oney twicet as much as before.

11 All the kinfoke cum back, and brung bred and simpathy, and comfert him fer what he bin thru, and they past round the hat and give him munny and goldrings.

12 And God blest his latterdays,

and he end up with a lot more live stock than he had before the boyls.

13 He also got a new batcha son-sanddotters.

16 Jobe live on fer anuther hunnert and forty years.

17 When he died he was full of daze.

THE BOOK OF DAN YELL

CHAPTER 1

Y ou mind the time King Nabakid-nestor beseeched Jerussilem.

2 He tuck back to his land of Shiner a lotta boody.

3 He ast his yewnuck to bring along sum of the hire class of Izzreal peeple too.

4 Top grade peeple and their kids. Fed them up good, too. Givem lotsa pork chops.

8 One young fella, Dan Yell, didden fantsy swine, so he beg off dinner.

10 The mane yewnuck tole Dan Yell it mite put ther heds in danger if the King found out. "Yule start to look poorly."

11 So Dan Yell sed:

12 "Lemme try my dyet fer ten days. Jist pulsin' water

13 After that check me out agin the meat eaters."

14 "Dun," sed the yewnuck.

15 Ten days later, Dan Yell look prittier and fatter than all them carnyvores.

16 Everybuddy after that went on a pulse dyet.

17 Dan Yell was smarter too, even in his sleep ware he had dreems and vizzyuns.

19 The King checkt him out.

20 Found Dan Yell ten time smar-ter than all his wisemen.

CHAPTER 2

N abakidnestor started havin bad dreems.

2 Called in his wisemen and sor-sers fer to give a reeding on them.

5 But he cooden member his dreems they was so bad. Reglar nitemayors. So he ast the wisemen to member his dreem for him.

6 If they cud tell him his dreem and what it meant, they was in fer nice surprizes. If not, cut-up into peeces on a dunghill.

7 So the wisemen sed, "Tell us yer dreem, deer King."

8 The King sed, "I tole you I don't member it enny more. You tell me.

9 And if you don't know it, why do you call yerselfs sears and sor-sers?"

10 They sed, "Ain't nobuddy kin do that trick, reedin a dreem which is fergot."

12 The King was fed-up and order all the wisemen to be deestroid.

13 Dan Yell he was figgered fer one of the wisemen, so he was in line fer this.

Nabakidnestor's grave imedge

16 He went strait to the King, and ast fer a littel time to whomp up what his dreem meant.

18 Then Dan Yell pray to God.

19 God giv him nite vizzyun.

20 Dan Yell sed, "Thank God.

23 Now I know what is rong with the King."

25 Dan Yell was whip up fast in front of the King.

26 The King sed, "Kin you do this what them wisemen can't?"

28 Dan Yell sed, "I cant, but I got a God who can.

31 You was in yer bed, King and you seen a grate imedge.

32 It was tairible, gold hed, silver brest, brass belly. Laigs of arn, feet of clay.

34 Sumbuddy cut a stone, no-hands, and knock that big mettle thing all to peeces.

35 The wind carry it all away, but the stone grew up into a big mountin and fill the hole erth.

36 That's the dreem. I'll tell you what it meens.

37 You, king, are big in every way.

38 Yer the big hed of gold.

39 After you stop rooling, a infeerier kingdum will take over. And anuther bunch of brass will take over after that.

40 Then arn men will take over after that. But they'll brake up soon.

43 But the hole thing will end up clay, and crumbel.

44 Then my God will take over.

45 He's the stone, He was made with no hands, and He'll be knockin off all yer kingdums startin with you."

46 The King fell on his face and worship Dan Yell fer a change. Tole servints to bring sweet oders fer Dan Yell.

47 He tole Dan Yell, "I wanna be on yer God's side."

48 Dan Yell was made a grate man, and rooler of Baby Lawn, in charge of all wisemen.

49 Dan Yell ast fer jobs fer his three frends, Shad Rack, Me Shack, and A-bend I Go.

CHAPTER 3

After that Nabakidnestor made a big imedge outa gold, six by sixty Cubans, and had it set-up.

2 He invit everybuddy to cum fer the deddicayshun.

3 Everybuddy and his bruther shoad up.

4 His harold cryed out, "All rite, everybuddy.

5 At the sound of yer cornit, floot, harp, sackbutt, saltery, sulsemerr, and that kinda mewsick, all fall down and worship it.

6 Them not fallen down gits to be part of the barbykew.

7 When they herd that cornit, floot, harp, sackbutt, saltery and like that, everybuddy fall flat.

12 Eggsepp Shad Rack, Me Shack, and A-bend I Go.

13 Nabakidnestor was in a fewry.

14 Nabakidnestor sed, "What's this I heer about you bunch?

15 Didden you heer the cornit, floot, harp, sackbutt, saltery, dulsemerr ett setterer? Flatten out, or you git made a fuel of fer my furniss. And I'd like to see ya git out of that."

17 Shad, Me and A-bend thot they knew Sumbuddy mite deeliver.

19 Nabakidnestor start to froth,

and order up sum heet. The thermostat was bent over the limit.

21 Then them three young fellas was throan into the fire with all ther cloze on.

22 It was so hot, the men throwin them in got bernt up.

24 Nabakidnestor cooden bleeve his eyes. "Didden I just have three boddys throan into that furniss?" "Sure thing, King."

25 "Then what are they doin all three ... no, four! wockin around loosly in there, like it wuz nuthin. And ... my God!!!" (That's who the forth one was.)

26 Nabakidnestor cum as close as he dair, and sed, "You boys cum out of thair. Yule ketch yer deth a heet."

27 But ther wuzn't a hare sinj on their heds. They dint even smell cookt.

28 So the King sed, "Bless my sole," and brung them out.

29 And he made a degree that everybuddy hadda speek good and bow down to the God of Shad Rack and Mee Shack and A-bend I Go. And if they dint, they wud be cut in peeces and castoff on a dunghill. Nabakidnestor he liked a God what deelivers.

30 Shad Rack, Me Shack and A-bend I Go got permoted back to ther ole jobs.

CHAPTER 4

Nabakidnestor had anuther dreem.

9 He ast Dan Yell to unravel it fer him.

10 He seen a big tree in yer middel erth.

11 The tree reech up to Hevvin.

12 The froot was grate, enuff meat fer everybuddy, all the cattel shaddered under it, and the berds sat on the bows.

13 Then sumbuddy cum down frum Hevvin, and yelled,

14 "Cut down the ole tree, shaik the leafs and scatter all the froots. And git those beests away frum under, and shoo them berds off.

15 Jist leeve a stump in the grass, and wet it with dew. That's all 'he's' gonna git.

16 And change 'him' into a beest and let him forge fer hisself."

18 "That's my dreem," sed Nabakidnestor. "What's it mean, Dan Yell?"

19 Dan Yell cooden open his mouth fer to speek he was so shock by this.

20 "Sir, that tree you sawed in yer dream, goin strait up to hevvin ...

21 Laid-in with froot, and meat fer all to eat, and fulla berds and cows under.

22 That tree is yew, King. On accounta yer grateness is that big."

23 "Yes, but who's that fella cum frum hevvin and orders me cut down? And stumps me, and wets me with dew?"

25 "Yer gonna be cut down to size, King, absolootly stumped, and hafta liv with the beests of the feeld, and git wet with them, and forge fer pastyour with them, till you find out who's Boss.

26 That's why they leeve yer stump, so's you kin start all over agin.

27 So King, I sudjest you brake off with yer sins rite now, and start showin mersey to the poor, if you wanna have enny peece a mind."

28 All this cum to pass, too.

29 A yeer laider Nabakidnestor was wocking in his paliss ...

30 Lookin at all he had bilt-up, and boastin about it.

31 When a voyce frum hevvin sed: "That dun it, King. Frum now on, call it kwits.

32 Hed fer the feelds and git down on all fores, and eat what you can."

33 It happen all rite. King Nabakidnestor got rite down to yer grass roots. His hares terned to fethers, and his nalcs turn to claws.

34 Until he was put to pastyour he never reelize he wuznt King Pin.

36 That's when he got his reezin back.

37 And he prazed Hevvin for it.

CHAPTER 5

After him, cum his son, Belle Shazzer. He luv to eaten drink.

2 He drunk outa the holey vessles Nabakidnestor had brung up frum the Jerussalem tempel.

3 Everybuddy was aloud to drink outa them, even konkybines.

5 In the middel of the party, sumbuddy, nobuddy knows who, rit sumthing on the wall.

6 This was consider notty. The King's nees knock together, and he felt loose in his loyns.

7 He ast fer all the soothsayers to cum in and reed the riting, and whoever dun it gits first prize ... a gold chane and a red dress, and gits to cum third in the kingdum.

8 All the wisemen line-up, but they sed they cooden reed ritin that was ritten so rottin.

10 The qween sed, "Don't worry. I know a hand-riting eggspurt.

11 He was in charge of all this in yer dad's time.

12 Send fer Dan Yell."

13 Dan Yell cum. Belle Shazzer ast him, "Are you the same one was brung by my father out of Joory?" Dan Yell give him the nod.

14 "I've even herd of you. And as far as whizdum, yer sposed to be full of it.

15 My wisemen seem to be all dummys.

16 You wanna try fer third place, a gold chane and a red dress?"

17 Dan Yell sed, "Keep yer dress and chane fer yerself. Ile read this off-the-wall stuff, and tell you what it means too.

18 My God give yer father his King job.

19 And yer dad reely Kinged it up.

20 Till his pride give him hardnin of the mind.

21 And he sunk down to beest-level, and made a wild ass of hisself.

22 Yer his son, and now it's yer tern to lern.

23 You stole all God's good plaitware, and prazed other gods with it durin drunk-in partys. God never got enny creddit.

25 You see what's on that wall?

MANY MANY TICKEL A PARSON

26 Tell you what that meens. MANY ... That's all. Yer finisht.

27 TICKEL ... Hands up, you lost.

28 A PARSON ... Divide up yer kingdum amung yer ministers."

29 Dan Yell wun third prize and pulled off the chane and red dress, too.

30 That nite Belle Shazzer died.

31 Dairyus the Median tuck over, age 62.

CHAPTER 6

Dairyus set up a hunnerd and twenny printses to be over his kingdum.

2 On top of them he pit Dan Yell to be first vice presdent.

3 The uther 119 got tairbly jellus.

4 They tride to sabbitosh his kareer.

5 They figgered the only way they cud finger him was at worship.

7 They got Dairyus to sine a statyoot what sed, 'Anybuddy settin up a partishyun to God er man fer the next thirty days will have to join the Lion's club.'

9 The king sined it. He cum from the Media, and being new to Pursya what did he know? To him, one man's Mede is anuther man's Pursian.

10 Dan Yell wuz in his house with the winders open, on his knees to God as wuz his wants, three times a day.

11 The jellus printses look-in thru the winder and cot him at it.

12 They tole the King Dan Yell was making a partishyun to God, and that was agin the bylaw he had jist sined.

14 The King cuda kick hisself when he herd this. He didden want to throw Dan Yell to the Lyins.

15 But all them printses sed, "If you sine a law it cant be outlawed."

16 So they brung Dan Yell and put him in the den. King Dairyus kept his fingers crost.

18 He went home, fast all nite and terned off the mewsick. Didden sleep a wink.

19 Got up erly and went to the zoo fer to see what the lyins had et.

22 But God had deelivered Dan Yell, by makin them lyins promiss to keep ther mouths shut.

23 The King laff up a storm, and Dan Yell cum out without a scratch.

24 But the lyins was reddy to eat if they cud git ther mouths open, and git ther teeth into sumthin. King Dairyus sent them breckfust: 119 printses, pluss wives and childern, so extry helpins was had by all.

25 King Dairyus rote: Peece unto you.

26 He made a new deecree. From now on, everybuddy hadda shaik with feer in fronta the God of Dan Yell. It made a nice change frum them lyins.

28 Dan Yell hung around even after Dairyus fell off his throan, and was replaice by King Sire-us.

THE BOOK OF JOANER

CHAPTER 1

God pass the werd on to one of his miner profits, Joaner.

2 The werd was, "Git up and go to Ninnyvuh. It's a grate city and I want you to complane at the top of yer voice aginst all them wicket Asseeryans."

3 Joaner didden wanna mix with all them forners so he thot he'd hide out from God in Tarshish. (FOOT-NOTE: He musta bin drunk at the

Dan Yell joins the Lyin's Club

time.) He tuck the fairy frum Jopper to Tarshish having paid his fair.

4 But you cant hide frum Him. He sent a ring-tail snorter of a hurrycain till the ship Joaner wuz in was like to be broken wether Joaner like it or not.

5 The sailers who wuz marrinatin the ship, heeve the cargo overbored. Joaner he was below stares, fast asleep.

6 The cappin cum down to him and sed "What in blazes are you sleepin for? Git up offa yer hammick and help pray fer God to take note of you, if He bothers with sich things."

7 The sailers figgerd sumbuddy had jinks the ship, so they had a raffle, and Joaner got the boob prize.

8 They sed, "Now we know whodunnit. Ware are you frum anywaze?"

9 Joaner aloud as he was a Heebrew, and fleeing frum God.

10 That put the wind up them sailers.

11 Havin no oil, they figgerd they better spred Joaner upon trubbled waters.

12 Joaner nod his hed. "It's my falt yer havin a ruff time. Mebby I kin smooth things over if you throw me in."

15 They dun it, and everything cammed down.

17 Eggsept Joaner. Fer he seen a big fish jawing tords him. It was brot up by God. And Joaner wuz booked in it fer three days and nites.

CHAPTER 2

Joaner kept hisself bizzy in that fishy belly. Praying a lot.

4 "I may be out of site, Lord, but I'm still kneeling at yer Tempel.

5 I'm soak to the skin and I'm over my hed, witch is rapp round with weeds.

6 I've reely hit bottom now. I musta bin pig-hedded.

8 I wuz a reel vannity case.

9 Sorry Lord."

10 God had a werd in the fish's ear, the fish threw up, and Joaner hit dry land.

CHAPTER 3

God give Joaner a secund chants.

2 "Git back to Ninnyvuh and preech what I tole you."

3 Ninnyvuh was a big trip. Three days.

4 Joaner step on the welcum mat, and yell, "Forty days, and counting. That's all you peeple got left!"

5 And the peeple beleaf him. They all went on fast time, and put on ther sack cloths. It was like a yewniform all over.

6 Even the king was warin it, wile he sat in his ashes.

7 And he put all them hy-living Ninnyvites on a strick dyet. No food, no water.

8 Everybuddy, man and beest had got into the sackcloth and tern ther dwelling into a reepent-house.

9 All this was dun hoping God wud be the first to reepent.

10 God seen all these goins on and reepent. What He had sed he wud do He did it not.

CHAPTER 4

Everybuddy was happy agin, eggsepp Joaner.

2 He didden like Ninnyvites and

Joaner brung up by a wale

wanted to go back Tarshishwords.

3 He thot he'druther die than stay amung all them silly Asseerians.

4 God sed, "What are you poutin about now?"

5 So Joaner went over to the eest side, and rented a booth, and sat under it, hopin the city wud fall around his ears.

6 God thot Joaner had had too much sun so He brung a big goord so that it hangover Joaner. Joaner give thanks fer the goord.

7 But God put a werm in that goord, witch went to work so that Joaner wunderd wither his goord went.

8 After sunup God sent a eestern wind, and between windburn and sunstroke Joaner fainted, and hoped it wud becum permamint.

9 God sed, "What are you fussin about, yerself or the goord?" And Joaner sed if he was gonna go goordless he mite as well die.

10 God sed, "Look at you, piddying a plant witch you never growed, or even hoed. It happen one nite, and was took away the next. Sich a fuss over nuthin.

11 Now why shood I not spair a grate city like Ninnyvuh, popillation a hunnert and twenny thousand persons not incloodin ther cattel, and not one of them knows a rite tern frum a left?"

THE BOOKS OF SAMS, PROVERBS, CLEAZY ASTYS and SONGA SALOMON.

These books is all fulla poetry. Even tho it don't rime it is luvly in itself and don't need enny help frum ennybuddy.

I-Say-Uh, Jerry Myer, Zeekyell, Ho Seeyuh, Jole, Aymiss, Obie Dire, Miker, Nay Him, Habbakook, Zeffernyuh, Haggy, Seckerire, and Mallerky. Every one of these is profits. A profit is sumbuddy gets up on a high place, looks down on everybuddy elts. No matter what ther name is, everyone of them profits seems to tell the peeple the same thing:

YER DOIN' IT ALL RONG!!!

A profit lookin down on everything

Most people who know Don Harron think that he is younger than Charlie Farquharson, but if the truth were known he is much, much older. Don Harron was born in 1924, but Charlie was conceived in 1942 when Don worked on a farm near Lindsay Ontario. The actual birth took place ten years later during the 1952 version of the Canadian revue "Spring Thaw." Medical science has no explanation for this.

Since the words "Parry Sound" seemed to bring out best the Northern Irish inflections (five generations removed) in Charlie's speech, Don Harron's alter ego was given the birthplace of Parry Sound, Ontario.

Charlie Farquharson would be glad to hear that Don Harron has finally got a day job (his first regular employment since leaving the Royal Canadian Air Force in 1945). He is now the host of CBC's "Morningside" and is heard all across the country five days a week from 9:15 to 12 noon.

This is too late for Charlie. Chores are over and he is either out standing in his field or sitting at the kitchen table writing books. Books like *History of Canada, Jogfree of Canada, the Whirld and Other Places* or *Charlie Farquharson's KORN Allmynack* keep him busily Gaged when it's too wet to plow.